SCIENCE

50 IDEAS IN 500 WORDS

This edition published in Great Britain, Australia and New Zealand
in 2019 by Modern Books

An imprint of Elwin Street Productions Limited
14 Clerkenwell Green
London EC1R 0DP
www.modern-books.com

Additional texts by Mark Frary, Ian Haydon and Kathryn Ross
Illustrations by Richard Burgess, Emma Farrarons and Joanna Kerr

ISBN 978-1-911130-76-5

10 9 8 7 6 5 4 3 2 1

Printed in China

SCIENCE

50 IDEAS IN 500 WORDS

PETER MOORE

Contents

Chemistry

Genetics and Microbiology

Introduction

The important thing is not to stop questioning. Curiosity
has its own reason for existence. One cannot help but be
in awe when he contemplates the mysteries of eternity, of
life, of the marvellous structure of reality. It is enough if one
tries merely to comprehend a little of this mystery each day.

Albert Einstein, *LIFE Magazine* (1955)

As a way of thinking, science has produced remarkable results.
Its method of attempting of make sense of the universe we live in
by not only asking questions but going on to performing carefully
organised data-generating experiments has let humans look inside
minute atoms as well as probe the vastness of space.

It wasn't always this way. Ancient thinkers tried to work
out how the world and the heavens worked by asking questions
and then using processes of dialogue and argument to come
to answers. Few thought that studying physical objects would
provide anything useful and until the 17th century, fewer still
made any attempts at accurate measurements.

There are, however, always a few exceptions, and a few key
individuals and groups living around the Mediterranean basin and
the Middle East well before the Christian Era developed complex
understandings of mathematics and used these to make some
staggeringly detailed studies of the sun and stars.

Spanning two and a half thousand years of civilisation,
Science: 50 Ideas in 500 Words gives you the stories behind the
brilliance, brainstorming, setbacks and formulae from cosmology
and mathematics, biology and medicine, physics and chemistry.

It lets you understand why these insights are of central
importance in your life.

This book highlights fifty of the men and women who have made many of the most remarkable discoveries, and in each case focuses on one or two of the contributions they made. It sketches the person's background and shows how their initial ideas developed into tried and tested theories. From there you will see how these theories have long-lasting influence, affecting our lives and the technologies we live with.

Through the book we discover how lines drawn in ancient sand influence the way that mathematicians today deal with trigonometry and 21st century engineers design structures. We see how sequences of scientists and their discoveries led to ever fuller understanding of features such as the make-up of gases, how they eventually harnessed the power of electricity, and tackled the microscopic bugs that cause infection. In the realm of mathematics, you will see the wonder of curious numbers like Pi, and may even develop a fresh appreciation of triangles.

The progress in science has been huge, the spin-offs immense, but this book shows that new ideas and insights are hard to predict, even though they may be just around the corner.

Peter Moore

Astronomy

The night sky, that canvas of black velvet jewelled with twinkling diamonds, has long inspired deep thinkers. From the earliest observers of the wandering stars of our skies to modern-day astrophysicists, scientists have delved into the field of astronomy in a bid to understand Earth's place in the universe.

The Solar System

The sun, with all those planets revolving around it and
dependent on it, can still ripen a bunch of grapes as if it had
nothing else in the universe to do.

Galileo Galilei

The Earth is a small but remarkable planet, set in the middle of a
small and probably unremarkable solar system, tucked into the
corner of a medium-sized galaxy which is just one of billions in the
universe. Working this out was no mean feat.

When the famous astronomer Nicolaus Copernicus (1474–
1543) viewed the heavens, he came to a radical conclusion: rather
than accepting the ancient view that everything revolved around
the Earth, he showed that another explanation for our observations
was that the Sun was the central object. When Johannes Kepler
(1571–1630) produced final proof for Copernicus' theory in 1621,
the concept of a Solar System became irrefutable.

Even so, there was much to discover. At the beginning of the
17th century, astronomers had only been able to spot eight bodies
that moved across the skies. These were the Sun, Mercury, Venus,
Earth and its moon, Mars, Jupiter and Saturn. Uranus wasn't
known of until William Herschel (1738–1822) spotted it in 1781,
Neptune was first seen by Johann Gotfried Galle (1812–1910) in
1846 and Pluto by Clyde Tombaugh (1906–1997) in 1930.

During this period various observers were beginning to detect
'moons' orbiting many of the planets. In 1610 Galileo Galilei
(1564–1642) spotted Callisto, Europa, Ganymede and Io all
orbiting Jupiter. It was a remarkable feat of observation, even
though he managed to miss the other 21 bodies that orbit that
faraway planet. Indeed each time we get a better view of the Solar
System we seem to find more objects to name and study. The twin

Voyager satellites that were launched in 1977 have gradually made their way through the Solar System, making close encounters with many of the planets as they travel. Between 1985 and 1989 Voyager 2 beamed back information about 16 newly identified major bodies in the Solar System, bringing the total known so far to 71.

At a distance of just under six billion kilometres, Pluto used to be regarded as the farthest planet from the Sun. However, in 2006 the International Astronomical Union (IAU) demoted Pluto to the status of dwarf planet. This decision was made not because of its small size, but because it shares its orbital neighbourhood with a series of small, icy bodies beyond the orbit of Neptune in a region known as the Kuiper belt. Pluto has not achieved gravitational dominance, and this meant it couldn't claim the label of planet.

As well as beginning to realise the intricacies involved in our own solar system, astronomers have started to see that this is just the start. Each star in the sky represents another sun, many of which we now know are orbited by planets of their own. Our solar system rests in one of the spiralling arms of a medium-sized galaxy that we call the Milky Way. It is about 100,000 light years across and contains some 100 billion stars. The Sun orbits around the centre of the galaxy, making one rotation every 225 million years.

It turns out that this galaxy is just one of billions of others found within the universe, some of which contain up to three trillion stars. On this scale, our solar system is tiny, for all that it is so important for us.

Aristarchus of Samos

The Greek astronomer Aristarchus, in the third century BCE, was already proposing the theory of heliocentrism – the idea that the sun is at the centre of the solar system. Yet his idea would not gain acceptance until Catholic cleric Nicolaus Copernicus arrived on the scene in the 15th century with a mathematical model for how such a solar system might work.

Born: Ca. 310 BCE Samos, Greece
Importance: Shifting Our View of the Earth
Died: 230 BCE Alexandria, Egypt

The commonly held assumption at the time was that the Earth sat at the centre of the 'universe', and that the whole universe had a radius of the distance between the Earth and the Sun. But Archimedes said that this idea was challenged by Aristarchus, who claimed that the universe was many times bigger, and that the Sun, not the Earth, remained fixed at its centre, with the planets orbiting around it.

At that time astronomers believed that all the stars were fixed in position in a single sphere, with the centre of the sphere being the Earth. It is as if the ancients thought they were living at the very centre of a huge ball that had thousands of tiny holes pricked in the surface allowing light to penetrate from 'outside'. Aristarchus' idea was new.

His 'heliocentric' idea had power, partly because it was an easy way of explaining why the stars always seemed to be in the same position relative to each other. If the Sun were the centre and we on Earth orbited around the Sun, then there should be an apparent shift in the relative positions of the stars. Aristarchus explained this problem away by saying that the distance between Earth and the stars was infinitely large in comparison to the distance between Earth and the Sun. In this case the shift would be so small that you would not be able to see it.

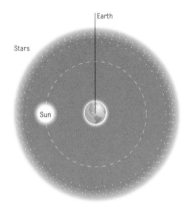

Stars

Earth

Sun

At the time no one took this theory particularly seriously. After all, pointed out Archimedes, this is based on the idea that the universe must be huge, and let's face it, it just can't be that big. Later scientists would realise that it is bigger than even Aristarchus thought.

His only surviving work provides some remarkably detailed geometric arguments that conclude that the Sun was about twenty times further from the Earth than was the Moon, and twenty times bigger than the Moon. He calculated this by working out the angles in the triangle formed by the Sun, Earth and Moon, when half of the Moon facing the Earth was illuminated. The Sun is in fact 109 times the size of the Earth and 400 times further away, but these errors come from the fact that his measuring instruments were poor; his basic calculations were fine. Aristarchus consequently showed that mathematics could help us see our place in the universe.

Claudius Ptolemaeus ('Ptolemy')

While people from different religions and cultures disagreed on many things at the time when Ptolemy was working, they were united on one thing – that the Earth was at the centre of the universe.

Born: Ca. AD 100, Alexandria, Egypt
Importance: Created incredible maps
Died: Ca. AD 170, Alexandria, Egypt

For some this was based on religious belief, for others the conclusion was drawn from philosophical arguments. Ptolemy therefore set out to pull together all previous observations, calculations and theories, and show how such a geocentric view might work.

When astronomers looked at planets they became aware that they didn't just move smoothly through the sky night after night. Instead there were times when they appeared to stand still for a bit, or even move backwards. Ptolemy's explanation was that while the planets orbited the Earth in circles that had centres close to the Earth's centre, they also moved in small circles, called epicircles.

To do his work, Ptolemy developed mathematical ways of relating lines and angles, and one of his findings has been handed down as Ptolemy's theorem. This shows that there is a fixed set of relationships in lengths of lines of a four-sided box drawn within a circle. The theory underpins much current trigonometry.

The system drew heavily on the work of Greek and Babylonian astronomers such as Hipparchus (CA. 190 BC–CA. 120 BC) and required 80 different orbits; the combination of these orbits produced the pattern of behaviour seen from Earth. This model of the universe held currency until the Polish scholar Nicolaus Copernicus' (1473–1543) heliocentric view was published in 1543.

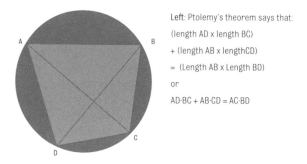

Left: Ptolemy's theorem says that:
(length AD x length BC)
+ (length AB x lengthCD)
= (Length AB x Length BD)
or
AD·BC + AB·CD = AC·BD

In addition to his work in astronomy, Ptolemy was a pioneering map-maker. Convinced that the Earth was a sphere, he developed geometric methods of projecting a sphere onto a flat surface. He also included co-ordinates of latitude and longitude for every feature drawn on the map, allowing anyone to reproduce it at any scale they wished.

Compared to modern maps, Ptolemy's look distorted, but even by the year 1500 his book *Geography* was so far ahead of anything else that it remained the principal work on the subject. His maps cover about a quarter of the world's surface, spanning from the Canary Islands in the west to China in the east, and from the Arctic to equatorial Africa. Indeed, *Geography* looked so convincing that it formed a critical part of the thinking that sent Christopher Columbus (1451–1506) sailing west in search of the Indies. Columbus thought that the journey would be short, because on Ptolemy's maps there was only a short span of ocean, but Ptolemy had underestimated the size of the Earth and had overestimated the size of Asia.

Tycho Brahe

'There is one heaven . . . ungenerated and eternal'. These are words from the astronomical writings of Aristotle and outline the view that was to remain unchallenged for the next 18 centuries. Until, that is, Danish astronomer Tycho Brahe, using the most advanced astronomical instruments of the pre-telescope era, built to his own designs, observed an event that was to change everything.

Born: 1546, Scania, Denmark [now part of Sweden]
Importance: Breaking the Celestial Sphere
Died: 1601, Prague, Czech Republic

The constellation of Cassiopeia is one of the most recognizable in the night sky, thanks to its distinct 'W' of bright stars. In the year 1572, this W was suddenly joined by something unexpected. Writing in the book *De Nova Stella*, Brahe explained his shock:

On the 11th day of November in the evening after sunset, I was contemplating the stars in a clear sky. I noticed that a new and unusual star, surpassing the other stars in brilliancy, was shining almost directly above my head; and since I had, from boyhood, known all the stars of the heavens perfectly, it was quite evident to me that there had never been any star in that place of the sky...

What Brahe had seen was a supernova, the last gasp of a dying star when its stock of nuclear fuel runs dry. It challenged the prevailing view of the perfection of the heavens.

Brahe had been drawn to astronomy by a 1560 solar eclipse and continued to study it in his spare time at universities in Germany and Switzerland. On his return to Denmark, he became absorbed in building highly accurate astronomical measuring apparatus such as quadrants, sextants and armillary spheres.

Left: The constellation of Cassiopeia is recognised by its distinction 'W' shape of stars. In 1572 it was joined by a new supernova which was visible to the naked eye. Brahe worked extensively to detail his observations of this 'new star' with significant implications for the ancient models of the heavens.

Yet the 1572 apparition changed everything. The publication of *De Nova Stella* was a sensation across Europe, showing that the long held Aristotelian view of the unchanging heavens was untrue. His services as an astronomer were suddenly in high demand and the Danish King offered him the island of Hven on which to build the world's greatest observatory, at a cost amounting to five percent of the country's gross national product.

With the best instruments money could create, he made meticulous observations of the stars, planets and comets. His observations of the so-called Great Comet of 1577 showed that comets were not atmospheric phenomena, as most people believed, but were far distant from Earth. These observations, and those he made of the planet Mars, were eventually used to show that heavenly bodies moved in elliptical, not circular orbits, shattering forever the illusion of celestial perfection and laying the foundations for Newton's theories of gravity.

Galileo Galilei

To be a free thinker is dangerous in any age. It becomes more problematic when your new ideas challenge established teaching, and when you compound this by acting with a lack of diplomacy.

Born: 1564, Pisa, Italy
Education: Padua University
Importance: Invented the telescope
Died: 1642, Arcetri, Italy

When Galileo Galilei headed off to Padua to study, medical education was still firmly based in the teachings and writings of ancients such as Claudius Galen (130–210) and Aristotle (BC 384–322), with little room given for injecting any new ideas. It is hardly surprising then that Galileo soon switched his attentions to the less restrictive world of mathematics.

He turned his mind to studying gravity. To slow down the action of gravity in order to better observe it, he ran a ball down a slope rather than simply dropping it. Galileo devised a water clock so that he could accurately measure short time intervals, and found that the time for the ball to travel along the first quarter of the track was the same as that required to complete the remaining three quarters. He realised that the ball was constantly accelerating. By repeating each experiment hundreds of times to see whether the same thing happened each time, he invented an important part of scientific method.

While sitting in Pisa cathedral one day he was distracted by a lantern that was swinging regularly at the end of a chain. He soon found that a pendulum takes the same amount of time to swing from side to side whether you give it a small push or a large push. The frequency only changes if you alter the weight, or change the length of the supporting rope.

Ever the inventor, Galileo developed a two-lens telescope and started studying the Moon, Sun and planets. He was the first person to see sunspots, the first to spot the four main satellites of Jupiter

Left: In Galileo's telescope, light rays from a distant object are brought to a focus by a convex lens. A second lens – the eyepiece – then spreads out (magnifies) the focused light so that it covers a larger portion of the viewer's retina, making the observed object appear larger than it actually is.

and the first to record that the surface of the Moon had mountains and craters. As he did this he started to look into the work of the Polish-born medic, lawyer and astronomer Nicolaus Copernicus (1473–1543), who in his 1543 landmark publication said that the planets, including Earth, rotated around the Sun. The Earth was not the centre of the universe.

Intrigued by the possibility, Galileo looked for evidence. He noticed that Venus went through phases, much like the phases of the Moon. From this he deduced that Venus must be orbiting the Sun. While he was right in his prediction he didn't have conclusive proof, and because it contradicted mainstream teaching, the Catholic church instructed him to stop talking about it. Instead he wrote a book presenting his ideas that included a thinly-veiled insult towards the Pope. The net result was that Galileo was put under house arrest for the rest of his life.

Johannes Kepler

Chiefly remembered for discovering three key laws of planetary motion and making some incredibly accurate astronomic tables, Johannes Kepler also made important discoveries in the fields of optics and mathematics.

Born: 1571, Weil der Stadt, Württemberg [now Germany]
Importance: Created incredibly precise astronomic tables
Died: 1630, Regensburg [now Germany]

With a father who was a mercenary soldier and a mother who was an innkeeper's daughter, Johannes Kepler's childhood was far from privileged. It was made worse when his father left home to fight in the Netherlands when Kepler was five, and never returned – presumed dead.

Intending to be ordained as a priest, Kepler went on to see his scientific research as a way of fulfilling a Christian duty to understand the works of God, saying at one point that he was merely thinking God's thoughts after him. He was convinced that God had created the universe according to some mathematical plan, and that mathematics would be the route to understanding it.

At Tübingen, Kepler started studying under astronomer Michael Maestlin (1550–1631). To teach some more advanced astronomy Maestlin introduced Nicolaus Copernicus' (1473–1543) recently published idea that the Sun, not the Earth, was the centre of the universe. It appears that Kepler instantly liked this theory.

He first developed a complex argument, suggesting that the paths of the planets could be predicted by calculating the sizes of a series of spheres, cubes and tetrahedrons nested inside each other. The arguments seem curious to 21st-century thought, but the results closely correlated with astronomical measurements.

Looking more closely, however, Kepler discovered that Mars' orbit was elliptical rather than circular, with the Sun one of the foci of the ellipse. He produced over a thousand sheets of mathematical

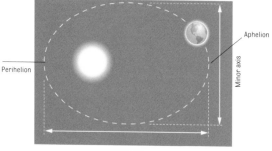

Perihelion

Aphelion

Minor axis

Major axis

Above: Kepler's second law states that the line joining the planet to the Sun sweeps out equal areas in equal times. Hence, the planet moves fastest when it is near perihelion (the point of nearest approach to the Sun) and slowest when it is near aphelion (the furthest point from the Sun).

workings before reaching this conclusion, and then proceeded to study the other planets. The fact that all the planets' orbits turned out to be ellipses became known as Kepler's first law of planetary motion. His second law was the realization that a line joining a planet to the Sun swept out equal areas in equal times as the planet travelled around its orbit.

Making good astronomical observations requires the best possible telescopes, so there should be little surprise that Kepler also became interested in optics. He discovered ways of making telescopes that used two convex lenses, a design so successful and widely used that it is simply called an astronomical telescope.

While Copernicus had presented the initial idea, and Galileo Galilei (1564–1642) had added some more observational data, it wasn't until Kepler had finished his work that for the first time there was mathematical and scientific proof that the planets orbited the Sun. The universe hadn't changed, but our understanding of it had.

Caroline Herschel

The comet-spotter Caroline Herschel was the first paid female astronomer in history, but her achievements have often been elided by those of her brother, William Herschel (1738–1822), who rose to fame for his discovery of the planet Uranus in 1781, the first planet discovered since antiquity. While she acted as his assistant, she was also a pioneering astronomer in her own right.

Born: 16 March 1750, Hanover, Germany
Importance: Discovered several comets
Died: 9 January 1848, Hanover, Germany

Contracting typhus at the age of 10, Caroline never grew past four foot three; on this basis her parents concluded she would never marry and trained her to be their house servant. She did not receive any sort of an education until her brother William – an established conductor in England – proposed she join him in Bath in August 1772 for a trial period as a soprano singer.

Professional musical life meant astronomy was initially just a hobby for the Herschel siblings, but William increasingly prioritized his nighttime searchings of the heavens, cataloguing double stars (pairs of stars that appear very close to each other as observed from Earth). Following William's groundbreaking discovery of Uranus, he was awarded with the office of court astronomer to King George III in 1782. Caroline was promoted as his official assistant, and was given an annual salary of £50 by the King in 1786 in recognition of her work.

Where the common telescope at the time was the refracting telescope, whose convex glass lens design made its image subject to distortion, the Herschel siblings built and developed reflector telescopes, pioneered by Isaac Newton (1643–1727), which used a single concave mirror instead of a lens, gathering more light and enabling a larger field of vision.

Using her own, small Newtonian reflector, Caroline discovered

14 new nebulae, as well as eight new comets between 1786 and 1787: cosmic 'dirty snowballs', or compounds of ice and dust, recognized by the visible atmosphere or coma that is produced when the body passes close to the Sun, as it warms and begins to release gases.

Some of Herschel's most important work was her *General Catalogue of Nebulae and Clusters of Stars*, published by the Royal Society in 1798. In her role helping to record William's observations, Caroline continually referred to John Flamsteed's mammoth catalogue *Historia Coelestis* (1725), 30 years in the making and containing information on nearly 3,000 stars. This process highlighted a series of discrepancies and errors. Caroline worked for over 20 months to provide a cross-index and updated the catalogue, entering 560 previously unrecorded stars.

Originally published under William's name in 1864, the catalogue would form the basis of *New General Catalogue* (NGC) in 1888, a numbering system which today provides the most commonly used label for these celestial landmarks – an indicator of the meticulousness of her calculations and recordings.

> I found an object very much resembling in colour and brightness the 27 nebula of the Connoissance des Temps, with the difference, however, of being round. I suspected it to be a comet; but a haziness coming on, it was not possible to satisfy myself as to its motion until this evening.
>
> Caroline Herschel

Fredrich Bessel

In January 1799, Fredrich Bessel left school to become an apprentice accountant in an import-export business. Interest in the countries his firm dealt with caused Bessel to study geography, Spanish and English in the evenings, and he started to ponder how a ship finds its way at sea. It was a short step from these musings to his developing a full blown interest in astronomy and mathematics.

Born: 22 July 1784, Minden, Brandenburg [now in Germany]
Importance: Charted 50,000 stars
Died: 17 March 1846, Königsberg, Prussia [now Kaliningrad, Russia]

In 1804 Bessel wrote a paper on Halley's comet in which he calculated its orbit using observations made by Thomas Harriot (1560–1621) in 1607. He sent his paper to leading comet expert Heinrich Olbers (1758–1840) who asked Bessel to make further observations and also asked him to consider becoming a professional astronomer. His response was to study celestial mechanics, firstly at the privately owned Lilienthal Observatory near Bremen and then at the newly built Observatory at Königsberg, where he remained for the rest of his life.

It was in Königsberg that Bessel determined the positions and relative motions of over 50,000 stars. His starting point was the data of English Astronomer Royal James Bradley (1693–1762). This work produced a system of predicting the relative positions of stars and planets. Bessel was one of the first astronomers to realize the importance of working out how many errors were involved in taking measurements. By working out all the sources of error that could be generated by Bradley's instruments, he created a much more accurate set of results. This enabled him to state the positions of stars on particular dates and eliminate from his reckonings such factors as the effects of the Earth's motion.

By eliminating all sources of error – optical, mechanical and meteorological – Bessel was able to obtain astronomical results

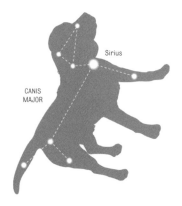

CANIS
MAJOR

Sirius

Left: From the erratic movements of Sirius, a star in the constellation Canis Major ('the great dog'), Bessel deduced the presence of an unseen companion star. Only after Bessel's death did astronomers finally see this 'dark star', confirming his prediction.

of astonishing delicacy from which a great deal of new data could be extracted.

In 1830 Bessel published data showing the positions of 38 stars over the 100-year period from 1750 to 1850. He spotted that two stars, Sirius and Procyon, moved somewhat erratically, and deduced that this variation in their movement must be caused by the tug of previously-unseen companion stars orbiting them. He announced in 1841 that Sirius had a companion, and was therefore the first person to predict the existence of so-called 'dark stars'. Ten years later the orbit of the companion star was computed, and astronomers finally managed to see it in 1862, 16 years after Bessel's death.

Bessel also worked out a method of mathematical analysis involving what is now known as the Bessel function. This helped him to analyze the way that the gravitational forces of three objects interact with each other as they move. The functions have now become an indispensable tool in applied mathematics, physics and engineering.

Edwin Hubble

In the 1920s most of Edwin Hubble's colleagues believed the Milky Way galaxy made up the entire cosmos. But peering deep into space, Hubble realised that the Milky Way is just one of billions of galaxies, and that these galaxies are all rushing away from each other.

Born: 1889 Marshfield, USA
Importance: Showed that the universe is huge and expanding
Died: 1953, San Marino, USA

Having studied science in Chicago and Oxford, Edwin Hubble started to examine the stars at Yerkes Observatory in Wisconsin before moving on to the prestigious Mount Wilson Observatory in California, which housed the world's most powerful telescope. The main focus of his attention was on strange, fussy clouds of light called 'nebulae'.

At Mount Wilson, Hubble found himself working alongside Harlow Shapley (1885–1972), an astronomer who had recently measured the size of the Milky Way. Using bright stars called Cepheid variables as standardized light sources, he had calculated that the galaxy was 300,000 light-years across – 10 times bigger than anyone had thought. Shapley was convinced that the Milky Way contained all of the stars and matter in the universe – that there was nothing beyond it. He believed that the luminous nebulae that interested Hubble were just clouds of glowing gas, and they were relatively nearby.

Equipped with his five senses, man explores the universe around him and calls the adventure Science.

Edwin Hubble

In 1924 however, Hubble spotted a Cepheid variable star in the Andromeda nebula, and using Shapley's technique showed that the nebula was nearly a million light-years away – a fact that placed it way outside the

Milky Way. We now know that this is the nearest of tens of billions of galaxies.

This alone didn't satisfy Hubble's curiosity. As he studied Andromeda, he realised that the light coming from it was slightly redder than he would have anticipated. The effect is similar to listening to the siren of a moving police car. As it approaches, the tone goes higher, and as it passes the tone drops. A shift towards red is equivalent to a drop in tone. The most likely cause of this so-called red shifting was that the galaxies were moving away from the Milky Way – our own galaxy. By measuring the shift in all the nebulae he could find, Hubble came to realise that the farther away a galaxy is from Earth, the greater the red shift – in other words, the faster it is moving away from us. The explanation was extraordinary: the entire universe is expanding.

Red shift: The light coming from distant objects is slightly redder than predicted. This red shift is best explained as a lengthening of the wave length of light caused by the universe expanding.

When Einstein heard of Hubble's discovery, he was thrilled. A decade earlier Einstein's new general theory of relativity had predicted that the universe must either be expanding or contracting. Astronomers had told him it was static, so he added an extra 'cosmological term' to account for the universe's stability. Hubble had demonstrated that this cosmological term wasn't needed, and that Einstein's own instincts had been right.

(Abbé) Georges Lemaître

Georges Lemaître was originally a priest and his interest in astronomy stemmed from his studies about creation, which, when combined with his scientific and mathematical work, led him to propose the Big Bang theory.

Born: 1894, Charleroi, Belgium
Importance: Introduced the Big Bang theory of the origin of the universe
Died: 1966, Louvain, Belgium

When he started studying the universe, most scientists thought that it was infinite in age and basically unchanged in its general appearance – that it had always been there. Scientists from Isaac Newton (1643–1727) to Albert Einstein (1879–1955) seemed to confirm that the universe had gone on for ever, stable and unchanging.

Lemaître wasn't convinced. Moving to do research at Cambridge, Lemaître reviewed Einstein's general theory of relativity and agreed with Einstein that the universe had to be either shrinking or expanding. Unlike Einstein, who added a cosmological constant to his equations to achieve a stable universe, Lemaître decided that the universe was expanding.

He believed this because the idea fitted with early observations of a red shift in colour of light from far off galaxies that Lemaître thought could be explained if these galaxies were moving away from us. Lemaître published his calculations and reasoning in 1927, but few people took any notice.

Two years later Edwin Hubble confirmed the existence of red shift and Lemaître then sent a copy of his ideas to Arthur Eddington (1882–1944), a member of the Royal Astronomical Society in London. The British astronomer realised that Lemaître had bridged the gap between observation and theory and the Royal Astronomical Society subsequently published an English translation of Lemaître's paper in 1931. Even so, most scientists agreed with Eddington that the idea of the universe having a beginning was repugnant. Cambridge astronomer Fred Hoyle (1915–2001) coined the term 'Big Bang' as a joke.

Lemaître knew that there were still some problems with his theory. To start with he predicted that the universe had expanded at a steady state, but this meant that it was expanding too quickly for the stars and planets to form. Lemaître solved this by using a variation of Einstein's cosmological constant to speed up the expansion of the universe over time. Einstein wasn't impressed. He had dismissed this constant as the worst mistake of his career and was upset to see anyone bringing it back to life. But in 1964 workers at Bell Laboratories in New Jersey became annoyed by a uniform microwave interference that kept being picked up by their radio telescope wherever they pointed it – at one point famously thinking it was caused by pigeon droppings building up in their radio telescope. Eventually, physicist Arno Penzias (1933–) realized that this microwave background interference was a remnant of the Big Bang.

Lemaître heard of this while in hospital recovering from a heart attack. He died two years later, knowing that his theory looked secure.

Big Bang: A theory of cosmology in which the expansion of the universe is presumed to have begun with a primeval explosion.

Einstein's Cosmological Constant: To achieve a static universe, Einstein added an artificial term, his cosmological constant, to his field equations that stabilised the universe against expansion or contraction.

Karl Jansky

Scientific advances are often made from unexpected discoveries; penicillin, X-rays and the smallpox vaccine are among just some of the 'accidents' that have led to monumental progress. Another such 'accidental' discovery of huge importance was made by radio engineer Karl Jansky when looking into possible sources of short wave radio interference.

Born: 1905, Norman, Oklahoma
Importance: Laid the foundations for radio astronomy
Died: 1950, Red Bank, New Jersey

Having graduated with a degree in physics from the University of Wisconsin, Jansky accepted a job as a radio engineer at the Holmdel site of telecommunications company Bell Labs. This was still in the early years of radio; Guglielmo Marconi (1874–1937) had sent his first signal just over 30 years earlier.

Bell asked Jansky to investigate possible sources of interference to 'short' waves (those with wavelengths of tens of metres), which could be used for transatlantic radio telephone services. Jansky built a bulky antenna – which became known as Jansky's merry-go-round because it could be rotated on a turntable – and he set about identifying sources of interference.

Jansky was quick to pinpoint two sources of static hiss: local thunderstorms and, slightly harder to work out, thunderstorms that were beyond visual range. However, another source of static, a low hiss, defied Jansky for a year. What was curious about the signal was that it seemed to vary in intensity with peaks occurring once a day. As a result of this daily cycle, Jansky started to believe that the sun may be the source of the interference. However, after months of observations, he noticed that instead of a cycle of 24 hours, the source actually had a cycle of 23 hours 56 minutes, suggesting an origin beyond the solar system.

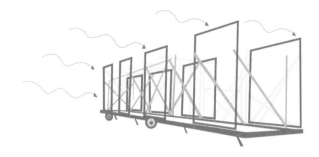

Above: Jansky's antenna does not look like the antenna we recognize today: this large structure rotated on its wheels so as to achieve all-sky coverage. Receiving waves at the frequency of 20.5 MHz, it enabled him to pick up on a low hiss which he identified was issuing from the heart of our galaxy.

Jansky's big leap was in recognizing that the interfering radio waves came from the heart of our galaxy, the Milky Way, in the direction of the constellation of Sagittarius. His findings were published in a paper called *Electrical Disturbances Apparently of Extraterrestrial Origin*, the word 'Apparently' included as a sop to his Bell superiors who were worried that they might be ridiculed. They need not have worried. Although Jansky was unable to continue his research into the Milky Way because his superiors wanted him to concentrate on telecommunications problems, he laid the foundations for the important subfield of astronomy that became known as radio astronomy.

Vera Rubin

Vera Rubin studied the mass visible in dozens of spiral galaxies, but each galaxy contained less mass than it needed to stop stars from flying off into space. From this, Rubin not only provided the first definitive evidence for dark matter but also provided evidence that the majority of mass in galaxies is something we can't even see.

Born: 23 July 1928, Philadelphia, Pennsylvania, USA
Importance: Provided evidence for the existence of dark matter
Died: 25 December 2016, Princeton, New Jersey, USA

In her early academic years, Rubin focused on studying the motions of galaxies and their distributions throughout the universe. It had recently been discovered by Edwin Hubble (1889–1953) that all galaxies (bar a handful of nearby galaxies) are moving away from us, with further galaxies moving faster. However, Rubin's work on discovering galaxy clusters and their motions showed there is also a 'sideways' motion of nearby galaxies, now known to be a part of our local galactic group. This is now widely recognised as evidence for large-scale structure in our universe, something which is only possible due to the presence of dark matter.

While working at Carnegie Institute of Washington, Rubin turned to individual galaxies, studying the rotations of several spiral galaxies similar to our own Milky Way. Using a new sensitive instrument called a spectrometer, she was able to spread the total light into its wavelengths, creating a kind of rainbow, called a spectrum.

According to the Doppler Effect, if the galaxy is moving away from the Earth, the light will be stretched and become redder. The reverse occurs if the galaxy is moving towards the Earth, making the light bluer. As a galaxy rotates, one side is moving towards the Earth, making the light bluer, the other moving away, making the light redder. The faster the galaxy rotates, the more the light is shifted. By comparing the spectrum of the galaxy from one side to the other, Rubin was able to calculate the rotational velocity of the stars within the galaxy as a function of their distance from the centre. What she found completely contradicted expectations and could not be explained by the visible mass in the galaxy alone.

According to Kepler's laws of planetary motion, the further you move away from the central mass a planet is orbiting around, the slower the motion of the planet. This is observed in our Solar System where Mercury orbits around the Sun much faster than Neptune. Since the majority of mass was expected to be in the centre of the galaxy, a similar pattern of velocity was expected as you moved further and further away from the central mass. However, Rubin found the stars on the outskirts of the spiral galaxies were orbiting at roughly the same velocity as those much closer to the central mass. Her elegant and simple solution: there must be a large amount of extra 'invisible' mass throughout the galaxy which is increasing the gravitational force and therefore the orbital velocities of the stars further from the centre of the galaxy.

Dark matter:
Hypothetical non-luminous material. It has not been observed directly but is believed to account for 85% of the matter in the universe.

Today, scientists have estimated all the matter we can see, named baryonic matter, makes up just 4% of the universe, while dark matter accounts for another 23% and the rest is dark energy.

Carl Sagan

Trained in both physics and biology, Carl Sagan spent his career studying the composition of nearby planets and the origins of biomolecules. His formidable scientific accomplishments were eventually eclipsed, however, by his own status as a public advocate for science.

Born: 9 November 1934, Brooklyn, New York, USA
Importance: Ground-breaking work on extra-terrestrial life
Died: 20 December 1996, Seattle, Washington, USA

Sagan studied the skies, had his own chemistry laboratory and wrote an award-winning essay on extraterrestrial life, all before graduating from high school. Sagan enrolled at the University of Chicago at the age of 16. There he earned four degrees, including a PhD in astronomy and astrophysics, as well as Top Secret clearance with the United States Air Force. As a student he trained under several Nobel laureates, including the geneticist Hermann Muller (1876–1931) and chemist Harold Urey (1893–1981). After holding an assistant professorship at Harvard for five years where he lectured and conducted research, Sagan transferred to Cornell University in 1968. He would remain a professor of astronomy at Cornell for the rest of his life.

Sagan published more than 600 scientific papers on topics ranging from the spontaneous formation of amino acids to the seasons on Mars. He was among the first scientists to posit the existence of water on Jupiter's moons, and helped identify the gaseous molecules that gave that planet its brick-like hue. He remains one of the most cited planetary scientists. But from his earliest days, Sagan was not content to remain locked inside an ivory tower. He wrote numerous popular books, including the Pulitzer Prize-winning *The Dragons of Eden*, which attempts to explain how human intelligence may have evolved. His lifelong connection to his country's space programme put him in position to brief the astronauts who first walked on the moon. And, ever a

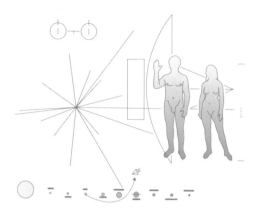

Above: Sagan designed the Pioneer Plaques that were placed on board the Pioneer 10 and Pioneer 11 spacecraft in the early 1970s. Designed to be universally comprehensible to alien life, these simple human figures offer a greeting of welcome and explanations about the position of Earth within our galaxy.

supporter of the search for extraterrestrial life, Sagan also helped NASA plan where on Mars to send robots.

Earth was never enough for Carl Sagan. As a public champion for science, he urged humanity to look upward – to the planets, solar systems and cosmos above. Late in life Sagan also became politically active around the issue of nuclear weapons proliferation which he saw as a threat to the continued existence of the species. He was twice arrested while protesting at nuclear weapons testing sites in Nevada.

Sagan died of pneumonia at the age of 62 with an unprecedented collection of awards, including NASA's Distinguished Public Service Medal, a Pulitzer Prize and two Emmys.

Stephen Hawking

Many people question whether humans will ever understand something as vast as the universe. Best-selling author and astrophysicist Stephen Hawking went further than most in developing theories that make sense of current data.

Born: 1942, Oxford, England
Importance: Developed a complex understanding of the nature of the universe
Died: 2018, Cambridge, England

While Hawking was born in Oxford, most of his academic life was spent at the University of Cambridge, first in the Institute of Astronomy and then at the Department of Applied Mathematics and Theoretical Physics. Diagnosed with a slow-progressing form of motor neurone disease at the age of 21, he spent much of his career developing Albert Einstein's theory of general relativity, which had introduced the concept of space-time. In special relativity and general relativity, time and three-dimensional space are treated together as a single four-dimensional concept called space-time. A point in space-time is called an event, and an event must have four reference points: length, breadth, and height and time.

Between 1965 and 1970 and working in collaboration with Roger Penrose (1931–), Hawking devised new mathematical techniques to study space-time and then went on to apply this to the study of black holes. These features appear to have been formed by stars collapsing in on themselves and becoming so dense, and their gravitational fields so strong, that amongst other things, light can not escape their pull. In 1970 Hawking showed that combining quantum theory and general relativity indicated that black holes can emit radiation. From then on he started working to try and roll quantum theory and general relativity into what people hoped would become a 'grand unified theory'.

A sign that this may be possible came when Hawking investigated predictions about the creation of the universe that flow from these two theories. He started by calculating that following the Big Bang many objects the size of a proton would be created. Whilst a proton is incredibly small, these particles might have a mass of as much as ten billion tons. The large mass of these mini black holes would give them huge gravitational attraction and therefore they would be governed by general relativity, but their small size would make them also governed by laws of quantum mechanics.

Hawking's mathematics also shows how it is theoretically possible that the universe can be finite, but at the same time have no boundaries or edge. One implication of this is a confirmation that laws of science can be formulated that completely describe the way the universe began.

In 1979 Hawking was appointed Lucasian Professor of Mathematics at Cambridge. The man born on the 300th anniversary of Galileo Galilei's (1564–1642) death now held Isaac Newton's (1643–1727) chair at Cambridge, a position he held until 2009. In 1988, he released his book *A Brief History of Time* which spent over 200 weeks on the *Sunday Times* bestseller list and won him international celebrity. In 2014, he allowed the use of his copyrighted computer-generated voice in the biopic *The Theory of Everything*.

By the end of his life, he had received 13 honorary degrees, been awarded the Copley Medal from the Royal Society and was director of research at the Centre for Theoretical Cosmology at Cambridge.

Quantum theory: The theory which describes laws of physics that apply on very small scales. The essential feature is that energy, momentum, and angular momentum come in discrete amounts called quanta. **Black hole:** An object with such high gravity that not even light can escape. Possibly formed when the most massive of stars die, and their cores collapse into a superdense mass.

Physics

The desire to understand how the
natural world around us works
and to construct laws and theories
that make concrete predictions
of how it might act in the future
was the genesis of the discipline of
physics. The great thinkers in the
following chapter went further in
doing so, from the very large scale
to the subatomic.

Nuclear science

There are two possible outcomes: if the result confirms the
hypothesis, then you've made a measurement. If the result
is contrary to the hypothesis, then you've made a discovery
  Enrico Fermi

Releasing even a small proportion of the energy stored inside
atoms can have an awesome consequence, but it can also be used
for peaceful means, as a source of energy.

The realization that there was a class of chemical elements that
spontaneously broke down to release energy and radiation gave
rise to a new branch of science that grew in importance through
the twentieth century. Before this, scientists had worked out that
materials were made of atoms, but had concluded that these atoms
were unable to change. Now they could see that under certain
circumstances some of them could change.

By 1934 Italian physicist Enrico Fermi (1901–1954) had shown
that neutrons could split many different types of atom. But the
results he got confused him because he found that adding the mass
of the resulting elements gave a result that was much lighter than
the original material. In 1938 German scientists Otto Hahn (1879–
1968) and Fritz Strassmann (1902–1980) produced similar results.

It was a combination of the Second World War driving all
these scientists to work in the USA, together with Einstein's
famous $E=mc^2$ equation, that triggered the next development.
Einstein's equation showed that it was possible for mass to
disappear, so long as energy was given out. At this point Niels
Bohr (1885–1962) also arrived in the USA, and joined an active
group of physicists who were discussing the possibility of creating
a sustainable chain reaction where the energy released by splitting
one atom could be used to split others, and so on.

On the morning of 2 December 1942, this group of scientists, led by Fermi, gathered at a squash court beneath the University of Chicago's athletic stadium. In the court they had built a cubic pile of graphite and uranium that had rods of cadmium running through it. The cadmium was included because it absorbed neutrons. They slowly started pulling the cadmium rods out and monitored the temperature of the stack. At 3.25pm the stack temperature rose and they allowed the rods to go back in – they had initiated a self-sustaining nuclear reaction and the world had entered the nuclear age.

While the first uses of this technology were military, with the 1945 bombing of the Japanese cities of Hiroshima and Nagasaki, the scientists were quick to turn their ideas into more peaceful applications. On 20 December 1951 in Idaho, USA, the first power station driven by nuclear energy began to produce electricity, and since then nuclear reactors have been built around the world.

The debate now rages as to whether we should make more use of nuclear power in producing electricity. It has a major advantage in that it produces no carbon dioxide or other waste gases that could contribute to climate change, but it has the disadvantage of producing small volumes of waste that will continue to emit radiation for thousands of years. It's a prime example of science generating a technology that seems almost too hot to handle.

Isaac Newton

Described in a school report as being idle and inattentive, Isaac Newton grew up to become a formidable mathematician and observer of the physical world. He described universal gravitation, laid the groundwork for classical mechanics and shares the credit for the development of differential calculus. Today, Newton is regarded as one of the most influential scientists in history.

Born: 1643, Woolsthorpe, England
Importance: Pioneering work on gravitation and mechanics
Died: 1727, London, England

Newton's early schooling may have appeared to be unproductive, but his head teacher pushed him towards Trinity College, Cambridge. In 1665 the plague swept across England, and the university closed months after Newton had received his first degree. Newton returned to Lancashire, where myth has it that he saw an apple fall to the ground and started thinking about the force that made it move. After performing a series of experiments, he concluded that two bodies, such as an apple and the Earth, or for that matter the moon and the Earth, attract each other with a force that you can calculate by multiplying the masses of the two bodies, and then dividing that figure by the square of the distance between them.

> If I have seen further it is by standing on the shoulders of giants.
>
> Isaac Newton

$$\text{Force} = \frac{\text{mass}_1 \times \text{mass}_2}{\text{Distance apart}^2}$$

Squaring values became a frequent aspect of physics equations. To start with Newton did it because it allowed equations to represent his observations. As future scientists began to explain gravitational fields the idea of squaring started to make physical sense. Gravity can be explained in terms of lines of flux radiating out in every direction from the centre of an object; and the more massive an object, the more lines of flux. At any distance from the object, the gravitational effect of these flux lines will be spread over the imaginary sphere that has its centre in the centre of the object. The greater the distance from the object, the larger the surface area of the sphere, and the more sparsely spread will be the 'ropes'.

As the area of the surface of the sphere is defined by the equation Area = $4\pi r^2$, a change that for example doubled the distance 'r' will quadruple (r^2) the surface area. The gravitational field will then be spread over this much larger area and will consequently be that much weaker.

In 1684 Newton started writing his most famous book, *Mathematical Principles of Natural Philosophy*. In this he extended his ideas and claimed to have identified three of nature's fundamental laws.

1. *That a body at rest, or in uniform motion, will continue in that state unless a force is applied.*
2. *That you can calculate the force applied to an object by measuring the object's weight and the rate at which it accelerates or decelerates.*
3. *That if one body exerts a force on another, the second body will exert an equal and opposite force on the first.*

This Newtonian understanding became the bedrock of physics for 300 years – and continues to have great value even now.

Alessandro Volta

A world without batteries is almost impossible to imagine, but when Alessandro Volta was born in Italy, no such thing existed. Although Volta didn't speak for the first four years of his life and his family became convinced that he had a mental disability, at the age of 29 he started teaching physics at the local high school, and within months of arriving at the school he had built his first invention.

Born: 1754, Como, Italy
Importance: Created the first electrical battery
Died: 1827, Como, Italy

Named an electrophorus, this device produced an electric charge from friction in a manner similar to the action of rubbing a party balloon on a sweater.

Soon Volta was promoted to Professor of Physics and three years later moved to a similar position at Pavia University. Here he came into contact with Luigi Galvani (1737–1798), a fellow researcher who had stimulated muscles in the limbs of recently dead animals using electricity. One day, while cutting a frog's leg, Galvani's steel scalpel had touched a brass hook that was holding the leg in place. The leg twitched. Galvani was convinced that this twitch had revealed the effects of what he called 'animal electricity' – the life force within the muscles of the frog.

Volta was sceptical and studied whether the electric current could have come from outside the animal. Volta discovered that bringing two different metals together sometimes caused a small electric current to run, and he correctly guessed that this had occurred when Galvani's scalpel touched the hook. The fact that you could produce electricity without the presence of animal tissue proved that Galvani's idea of animal electricity was wrong, but equally showed that muscles could respond to external stimuli.

Taking the idea further, Volta created a column of alternating silver and zinc discs. He separated the discs with sheets of cardboard

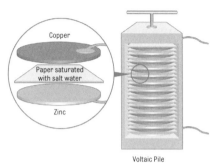

Voltaic Pile

Left: The Voltaic pile was the first electric battery. Volta placed together several pairs of copper and zinc discs separated by brine-soaked cloth and noted that the metals and chemicals in contact with each other produced an electrical current.

soaked in salty water. This stack produced a constantly flowing electric current, and building stacks of varying numbers of elements produced more or less powerful currents. His largest column consisted of 60 layers, but he soon found that having more than 20 elements in the stack produced a current that was painful if you held on to wires attached to either end.

What Volta didn't know was that all metals hold on to their electrons with different degrees of tenacity. If you place two different metals next to each other, electrons will flow from the one that is relatively more keen to give them up – this is the start of an electrical current.

Volta's contribution to the understanding of electricity was so significant that a key measurement of electricity, the volt, was named after him.

Electron: A negative charged particle that orbits the nucleus of an atom.

Michael Faraday

Born in the area of London now called Elephant and Castle, Michael Faraday grew up in a poor, but highly religious environment that led him to expect to find a unifying order in the way the world was made. He was brilliant and determined; to him we owe the discovery of electromagnetic conduction.

Born: 1791, Newington, England
Importance: Pioneered work in electricity and magnetism
Died: 1867, Hampton Court, England

Aged 14, Faraday started work as an apprentice bookbinder, but enjoyed reading the books more than binding them. In one book he found instructions that enabled him to build his own electrostatic machine. He soon joined the City Philosophical Society, which met every week to hear and discuss lectures on scientific topics. After attending a Royal Institution lecture given by Humphry Davy (1778–1829), Faraday became Davy's chemical assistant and toured the continent as Davy's valet. Among many scientific luminaries he met on his travels was the aged Volta, who inspired Faraday to investigate electricity when he returned to London in 1815.

In 1820 the Danish natural philosopher Hans Christian Øersted (1777–1851) wrote a paper describing how a compass needle deflects from magnetic north when an electric current is switched on or off in a nearby wire. This showed that electricity passing through a wire generated a magnetic field. In 1821 Faraday took this a step further. He pushed a piece of wire through a cork and floated the cork on water. The ends of the wire made contact with blobs of mercury and through these he was able to transmit electricity to the wire. When a magnet was nearby the wire moved each time he applied a current. Bending the wire, he found a way of making it and the cork rotate when he fed electricity through it and hence discovered electromagnetic rotation, a discovery that led to the invention of electric motors.

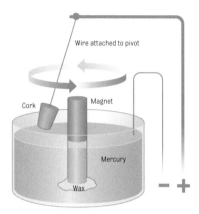

Left: By passing electricity through a wire in the presence of a magnetic field, Faraday found that a floating cork attached to the wire could be compelled to rotate – a discovery that led to the invention of the electric motor.

Convinced that energy was always conserved within a system, he decided that if electricity could produce a magnetic field, the reverse should also be true – magnetism should be able to produce electricity. It wasn't until almost 10 years later that he showed that moving a powerful magnet near to a coil of wire could cause a brief pulse of electricity to flow in the wire – he had discovered electromagnetic induction, the principle behind the electric transformer and generator. This discovery allowed 19th-century scientists to turn electricity from a scientific curiosity into a powerful technology.

As Faraday gained fame and reputation he never forgot the excitement of science he had felt as a child, and in 1826 gave the first Royal Institution Christmas Lecture for children – a series that still carries on to the present day.

James Clerk Maxwell

In the world of physics, the two greats of all time are with little doubt Isaac Newton (1643–1727) and Albert Einstein (1879–1955). Although the two were studying the same phenomena – motion and gravity – the theories they came up with could hardly be more different. One scientist more than any other made their theories possible, James Clerk Maxwell.

Born: 1831, Edinburgh, Scotland
Importance: Unified the theories of electricity, magnetism and light
Died: 1879, Cambridge, England

Maxwell was something of a polymath. At the astonishingly young age of 14, he wrote a remarkable paper on the mathematics of ellipses before going on to study at the University of Edinburgh and Trinity College, Cambridge.

In 1856, just a year after graduating from Trinity with a degree in maths, he published one of his seminal scientific papers, *On Faraday's Lines of Force*. In this he showed how the electromagnetic field proposed by the scientist Michael Faraday (1791–1867) could be treated mathematically in what have since become known as Maxwell's equations.

We have strong reason to conclude that light itself (including radiant heat, and other radiations if any) is an electromagnetic disturbance in the form of waves propagated through the electromagnetic field according to electrocmagnetic laws.

James Clerk Maxwell

The years 1861 and 1862 cemented Maxwell's reputation as a giant in the world of physics. It was at this time that he published a famous four-part paper entitled *On Physical Lines of Force*. In it, he was to make what is arguably his most important observation. Not content with having established a

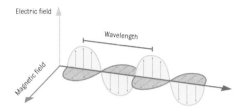

Electric field

Wavelength

Magnetic field

mathematical basis for the theory of electromagnetism, he went on in these papers to make a calculation of the speed of propagation of electromagnetic fields. Finding that the speed he obtained was close to the recently established speed of light, he wrote: 'We can scarcely avoid the conclusion that light consists in the transverse undulations of the same medium which is the cause of electric and magnetic phenomena.' This leap of insight provided the bridge between the work of Newton a few centuries before and Einstein a few decades later.

Maxwell also went on to show that temperature is a result of molecular motion, one of the key planks in the study of thermodynamics to this day.

Wilhelm Röntgen

Some people are prolific problem solvers. Among the problems Wilhelm Röntgen studied were the curious electrical characteristics of quartz, the influence of pressure on the way that fluids refract light, the modification of the planes of polarised light by electromagnetic forces and the way that oil spreads on water. But he is best remembered for discovering x-rays.

Born: 1845, Lennep, Prussia (now Remscheid, Germany]
Importance: Discovered x-rays
Died: 1923, Munich, Germany

With a Dutch mother and a German father, Röntgen was born in the lower Rhine province of Germany, but moved to Apeldoorn in the Netherlands when he was three years old. He showed no particular skills while at school, but in his spare time enjoyed studying nature and building machines. When he had the opportunity of going to university he studied engineering, but soon switched to physics and in time became Professor of Physics at Würzburg.

In 1895 he was studying what happened when he passed an electric discharge through a chamber containing gas of extremely low pressure. Previous work had shown that doing this with very high voltages could generate a stream of particles that became known as cathode rays. Such chambers have since been refined to form the cathode ray tubes in conventional television screens, and we now call the particles electrons.

On the evening of 8 November 1895, Röntgen enclosed the discharge tube in a thick black carton to exclude all light. When he turned off all the lights in the room, a paper plate coated with barium platinocyanide suddenly became fluorescent. He soon found that the radiation causing this was emitted when cathode rays struck the glass end of the tube, and that these rays had a much greater range in air than the cathode rays did. The plate glowed even when it was two metres from the tube.

Left: Different body tissues absorb X-ray radiation at different rates. When a photographic plate is exposed to these X-rays, dense objects such as bones, which allow fewer rays through to the film, show up as white 'shadows'.

Intrigued by these rays, Röntgen placed objects of different thickness in their path and found that they exposed photographic plates to varying degrees. Then one day he placed his wife's hand just in front of a photographic plate and shone the rays on it for a short time. When he developed the plate, the result was stunning. There was a ghostly outline of the hand, but the plate also revealed an image of the bones inside her hand and a clear mark caused by a ring she was wearing. It was the first 'Röntgenogram' ever taken, and gave doctors an unprecedented ability to look inside people's bodies.

In further experiments, Röntgen went on to discover that the new rays were produced when cathode rays hit a material object. Because the nature of these rays was unknown, he called them x-rays. Later, Max von Laue (1879–1960) and his pupils showed that, like light, x-rays are a form of electromagnetic radiation. The difference is that they have a shorter wavelength than visible light.

Heinrich Hertz

Born in Hamburg, Germany, Heinrich Hertz studied at the Universities of Munich and Berlin, and started working with a group of eminent physicists that included Hermann von Helmholtz (1821–1894). While there, Hertz completed a PhD on electromagnetic induction in rotating spheres.

Born: 1857, Hamburg, Germany
Education: University of Munich and Berlin
Importance: Made sense of electromagnetic radiation
Died: 1894, Bonn, Germany

In 1883 Hertz became a lecturer in theoretical physics at the University of Kiel. Here he studied the recent electromagnetic theory of James Clerk Maxwell (1831–1879). This theory was based on unusual mechanical ideas about the 'luminiferous ether'. This ether was a hypothetical substance supposed to fill all 'empty' space, and was thought to be the material that allowed light to travel through the universe. While another scientist performed some intriguing experiments that proved that this ether didn't exist, Hertz looked at the equations used to make sense of electromagnetic theory. He found that you could reconstruct these so that the idea no longer required ether. Electromagnetic theory had just taken a huge step forward.

> One cannot escape the feeling that these mathematical formulas have an independent existence and an intelligence of their own, that they are wiser than we are.
>
> Heinrich Hertz

Moving to be Professor of Physics at Karlsruhe University in 1885, Hertz soon discovered the photoelectric effect – where ultraviolet radiation knocks electrons from the surface of metal and creates an electrical current – which is now the basis of many photovoltaic cells used on items from satellites to road signs.

Although Hertz realised the significance of the photoelectric effect, his attention was drawn elsewhere. In 1888, in a corner of his classroom, he generated electric waves using a circuit consisting of a metal rod that had a small gap in it. The gap was small enough for the circuit to be completed by sparks jumping across it. Hertz then showed that these sparks triggered waves of radiation that could be picked up on a second, similar set of apparatus some distance away in the room.

In further experiments he showed that, like light, the waves could be focused or reflected, and that they could pass straight through non-conducting materials. Originally called Hertzian waves, we now think of them as radio waves. Hertz saw no practical use for the discovery, but others were quick to see the relevance. An English mathematical physicist, Oliver Heaviside (1850–1925), said in 1891, 'Three years ago, electromagnetic waves were nowhere. Shortly afterward, they were everywhere'.

The end result was that a young Italian by the name of Guglielmo Marconi (1874–1937) heard about Hertz's discovery while on holiday in Austria. He rushed home and started developing the idea until he could transmit a signal for more than one mile. In 1901 Marconi transmitted a signal across the Atlantic from Cornwall to Newfoundland, and radio came of age.

Electromagnetic radiation: A propagating wave in space with electric and magnetic components. Electromagnetic radiation is also used as a synonym for electromagnetic waves in general including, for example, light travelling through an optical fibre. Electromagnetic (EM) radiation carries energy and momentum which may be imparted when it interacts with matter.

Max Planck

It is frequently the case in science that a deviation from the expected result based on an existing theory leads to a new theory that fits the observed results much better. It was just such a situation that led the German physicist Max Planck to suggest a new way of thinking that gave birth to the field of quantum mechanics.

Born: 1858, Kiel, Germany
Importance: Launching the Quantum Theory
Died: 1947, Göttingen, Germany

While studying at the Universities of Munich and Berlin for a doctorate in philosophy, Planck was taught by Gustav Kirchhoff (1824–1887), famous for his work on electrical circuits but also for the conception of black bodies, idealized objects in thermal equilibrium that absorb all the radiation that falls on them. Such objects are a useful model in physics although the construction of a true black body remains in the realms of science fiction.

Many scientists at the time were interested in black bodies. In 1900, the British physicists Lord Rayleigh (1842–1919) and Sir James Jeans (1877–1946) proposed a law based on classical thermodynamics that sought to explain the radiation from a black body at various wavelengths. The problem was that, although the law gave very good results for radiation of long wavelengths, it produced nonsense for short wavelength radiation. This problem was later dubbed the 'ultraviolet catastrophe'.

We have no right to assume that any physical laws exist, or if they have existed up until now, that they will continue to exist in a similar manner in the future.

The Universe in the Light of Modern Physics

In the same year, Kirchhoff's former student Max Planck – who shared his professor's fascination with black body radiation – derived a new law based on empirical observations that did not suffer the same catastrophe, agreeing well with results at both short and long wavelengths.

Later that year, Planck reformulated his theory to incorporate statistical mechanics, including the postulate that the energy of electromagnetic radiation was 'quantized' – meaning that it could only take a series of allowable values rather than any value from a continuous range. This energy (E), he suggested, was proportional to the wavelength of the radiation (f) via the relationship $E = hf$; h is now known as the Planck constant.

Five years later, Albert Einstein (1879–1955) was to show that quantization of energy was indeed a reality through his explanation of the photoelectric effect. Planck, with the help of Einstein, thus kick-started a branch of physics – quantum theory – that began to challenge many concepts of classical physics.

Quantum mechanics:
The body of scientific laws that describes the behaviour and matter of very small, subatomic particles (for example, photons and electrons). Whereas classical mechanics deals at the scale of atoms and electrons, where objects exist in a specific place at a specific time, in quantum mechanics objects are in constant movement and cannot be so stably located.

Marie Curie

At a time when few women had the opportunity to experience the excitement of scientific research, Marie Curie introduced the world to the marvels of radioactivity. Her groundbreaking work sadly led to her death, as she had no way of knowing that radiation emitted from the materials she studied could trigger cancer.

Born: 1867, Warsaw, Poland
Importance: Discovered radioactivity
Died: 1934, Sallanchen, France

Born Maria Sklodowska, Marie grew up in Warsaw but broke free from the oppressive Russian political system – which did not allow women to go to university – by moving to Paris, where she registered her name as Marie on arrival. Here she excelled in physics and maths and in 1894 was introduced to the Laboratory Chief at the Paris Municipal School of Industrial Physics and Chemistry, Pierre Curie, whom she married the following year.

Initially Marie researched the magnetic property of steels. Her focus changed in December 1895 when German physicist Wilhelm Röntgen (1845–1923) discovered X-rays and, almost simultaneously, Frenchman Henri Becquerel (1852–1908) found that minerals containing uranium also gave off unknown rays. While many scientists concentrated on Röntgen's works, Marie studied Becquerel's uranium rays. Setting up a laboratory in a damp storeroom in the Paris Municipal School where Pierre was now a professor, she used a highly sensitive instrument which could measure tiny electrical currents that pass through air that has been bombarded with uranium rays. She discovered that the strength of the rays coming from a material depended only on the amount of uranium it contained. In addition, the electrical effects of the uranium rays were unaffected if you pulverised the uranium-containing material, kept it pure, reacted it to form a

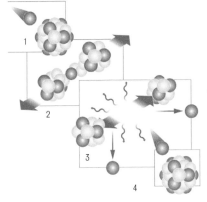

Left: In the reaction shown, a Uranium 235 nucleus is struck by a neutron (1). After absorbing the neutron to become Uranium 236, it splits to form two similar nuclei (2). The split generates huge amounts of radiant energy as well as neutrons (3) that start the process again (4), splitting other nuclei.

compound, presented it wet or dry, or exposed it to light or heat. Her conclusion was that the ability to give out rays must be a fundamental feature of uranium's atomic structure.

Curie then discovered that other materials gave off rays, and called the phenomenon radioactivity. When she found that a compound called pitchblende gave off more rays than was predicted from the amount of uranium in it, Pierre joined in her research. Together they discovered two new elements in the pitchblende, naming them polonium and radium.

These findings were controversial, but industrial companies started seeing potential in the work. Already they knew that the rays had value in medical imaging, but Marie started to show that they could damage biological tissue, a finding that led to their use in combating cancer. Marie also became aware that radioactive materials were often a source of heat, and started to speculate about the power that was potentially locked up in such substances – energy that other scientists would realize could be released in nuclear power stations and in deadly weapons.

Ernest Rutherford

When Ernest Rutherford died suddenly in 1937, the *New York Times* wrote: 'In a generation that witnessed one of the greatest revolutions in the entire history of science [Rutherford] was universally acknowledged as the leading explorer of the vast infinitely complex universe within the atom, a universe that he was first to penetrate'.

Born: 1871, Spring Grove, New Zealand
Importance: Made sense of atoms
Died: 1937, Cambridge, England

Following his rural upbringing in New Zealand, Rutherford went on to study and research at several key universities around the world. But it was while in his native country that he developed simple but effective switching mechanisms and monitoring equipment to determine whether iron was magnetic at very high frequencies of magnetizing current.

After three failed attempts to get into medicine, Rutherford succeeded in picking up a grant to study science and found himself working with Joseph John Thomson (1856–1940) in Cambridge University's Cavendish laboratory. Here Rutherford adapted his detector of 'fast transient circuits' and used it to investigate some of the properties of insulating materials. Impressed with his ability, Thompson invited him to join a select team studying the electrical conduction of gases.

During this work, Rutherford discovered that there were two distinct forms of rays coming from radioactive elements. Passing a beam of such rays through a magnetic field, he quickly saw that some were bent, while others travelled straight on. The ones that went straight on he called alpha particles – which are in fact helium atoms with their electrons stripped off – while those bent by the magnetic field he called beta particles, which turned out to be electrons.

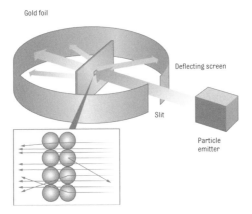

Gold foil

Deflecting screen

Slit

Particle emitter

Above: By firing tiny alpha particles at thin films of gold, and measuring the resulting deflections, Rutherford deduced that the mass of the gold atoms must be concentrated in an incredibly tiny, dense nucleus.

Moving to McGill University in Montreal, Canada, Rutherford discovered radon, a chemically unreactive but radioactive gas, and published his first book on radioactivity.

It was when he returned to England, this time moving to the University of Manchester, that he had an insight that would change our appreciation of the world. He'd given a student a laboratory practical to run, in which they fired alpha particles at thin films of gold. While most of the particles shot through the gold leaf a few were deflected, while one or two bounced straight back. Rutherford said that this was as if a large naval artillery round had been deflected by a piece of tissue paper.

In 1911 he deduced that this could only have occurred if the mass of the gold atoms was contained in an incredibly tiny nucleus. It was left to a young Danish scientist, Niels Bohr (1885–1962) to add that the rest of the atom would consist of a halo of electrons flying around the nucleus, much in the way that planets orbit around a star.

Albert Einstein

Few people have left such a large mark on the public mindset as Albert Einstein. Born in Germany into a Jewish family, Einstein had little success at school and showed no signs of becoming an international superstar until 1901, when he took a temporary job as Technical Expert, Third Class in the patent office in Bern, Switzerland.

Born: 1879, Ulm, Württemberg [now Germany]
Importance: Introduced the theories of special and general relativity
Died: 1955, Princeton, USA

His private life at the time was complex. In the same year that he started work in the patent office, his Hungarian girlfriend Mileva became pregnant. Conceiving outside of marriage was taboo, so they gave their child up for adoption, before marrying a couple of years later and then divorcing in 1914. In 1919 he married again, this time to Eva, his cousin, but it appears he was not an easy person to live with. In addition, his cultural roots were frequently disturbed. Having started off with German citizenship, Einstein renounced it and became stateless before taking Swiss citizenship. He later reclaimed German citizenship, but the Nazis revoked this because he was a Jew. Finally he moved to America and became a citizen of that nation.

Out of this chaotic life came some stunning scientific insights. In 1905, while working at the patent office, Einstein submitted four papers for publication. His papers on Brownian motion, the photoelectric effect and special relativity are all probably worthy of winning Nobel prizes, and indeed the Nobel committee did award him the 1921 Prize in Physics for his work on the photoelectric effect. But while the photoelectric effect and Brownian motion had given massive support to those claiming that atoms existed, relativity was something entirely new.

At first he introduced the idea of special relativity, in his 1905 paper 'On the Electrodynamics of Moving Bodies'. This theory integrated time, distance, mass and energy and was consistent with electromagnetism, but omitted the force of gravity. It challenged and overturned Newtonian physics by showing how the speed of light was fixed, and was not relative to the movement of the observer. One of the strengths of special relativity is that it can be derived from only two premises:

1. *The speed of light in a vacuum is a constant (specifically, 299,792,458 metres per second).*
2. *The laws of physics are the same for all observers in inertial frames.*

Special relativity: Einstein's theory that challenged Newtonian physics by showing how the speed of light was fixed, and was not relative to the movement of the observer.

Despite its simplicity, it had startling outcomes. Special relativity claimed that there is no such thing as absolute concepts of time and size; observers' appreciation of these features were relative, said Einstein, to their own speed.

In 1915 he took the idea further and developed a theory of general relativity. According to this theory gravity is no longer a force, but a consequence of what he called the curvature of space-time. Unlike special relativity, where reality is different for each observer, general relativity enables all observers to be equal even if they are moving at different speeds.

The ideas are mind-bending, but even though parts of them have been challenged, they formed the grounding for physics throughout the 20th century.

Niels Bohr

Ask someone to draw an atom and they will most likely sketch the classic 'solar system', with a large blob in the middle (the nucleus) and a group of smaller, orbiting dots (a cloud of electrons). Introduced over a hundred years ago by Ernest Rutherford (1871–1937), this model was the most successful of a range of ideas at the time. The only problem was that the model did not work in practice, and it took the Danish physicist Niels Bohr to work out an explanation.

Born: 1885, Copenhagen, Denmark
Major achievement: Increasing understanding of the atom
Died: 1962, Copenhagen, Denmark

In 1911, Bohr was becoming absorbed in the relatively new field of subatomic physics. Sir J. J. Thomson (1856–1940) had discovered the electron in 1897, while in 1911 Ernest Rutherford's experiments with alpha particles had thrown light on the existence of the atomic nucleus. Bohr was lucky enough to visit both Thomson at Cambridge's Cavendish laboratory in 1911 and Rutherford in Manchester in 1912, learning more of the latter's 'solar system' model of the atom.

Technology has advanced more in the last thirty years than in the previous two thousand. The exponential increase in advancement will only continue.

Niels Bohr

The problem with the Rutherford model was one of energy. According to classical theories of physics, an electron orbiting a nucleus would gradually lose energy, spiralling in towards it and ultimately crashing into it. Since we are all still here, we can surmise that atoms are inherently stable. The other problem with this model is that

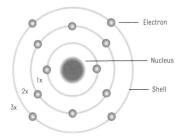

Electron

Nucleus

Shell

1x
2x
3x

Left: Bohr explained that electrons move in fixed orbits of electron shells at different distances away from the nucleus. The energy of electrons in each shell increases proportionally according to its distance from the nucleus.

the radiation emitted by an electron spiralling to its doom would increase in frequency: this did not agree with observations either.

Bohr's improvement on the Rutherford model was to draw from the work of Max Planck (1858–1947) and suggest that electrons travelled in orbits around the nucleus but could only have specific energies; energy was not continuously lost but only radiated when an electron jumped from one orbit to another.

While Bohr's proposal could have been seen as a clever tweak to hide a problem, his model's success lay in its explanation and also in its agreement with observed physical properties of atoms, specifically emission lines in the atomic spectra of hydrogen atoms that could be explained by electrons jumping between Bohr's allowed orbits. It is little wonder then that the science world heartily embraced Bohr's revolutionary ideas.

Werner Heisenberg

When Newton looked at forces and movement he saw predictability, and developed explanations for everyday events. When Einstein reinvestigated the same issues he concluded that reality was more complex, but it could be predicted if you took enough measurements. When Werner Heisenberg helped found quantum theory, he took physics into a world that was much less certain.

Born: 1901, Würzburg, Germany
Importance: Established the uncertainty principle
Died: 1976, Munich, Germany

In the 1920s Germany was an exciting place to work if you loved physics. While still in his early twenties Heisenberg met with the world's biggest names, debating and refining their work. He met Albert Einstein (1879–1955), Niels Bohr (1885–1962), Linus Wolfgang Pauli (1900–1958), and Max Born (1882–1970). Through their inspiration he looked again at the atom. Current theories speculated that electrons orbited a nucleus, much in the way that planets orbit the sun. As he collected data about the way that atoms emit and absorb light he came up with a radically new idea.

Called 'quantum mechanics', the new ideas were hotly disputed, but they drew together the mathematics of matrices with the physics of wave mechanics. Attracted to the world centre of debate, Heisenberg moved to Copenhagen to join Bohr's group of pioneering physicists. Here he spent a lot of time with Erwin Schrödinger (1887–1961) who visited frequently, and who was also actively trying to make sense of this area of physics.

The more Heisenberg studied the mathematics, the more curious he became. He realised that if you knew the position of an electron, you couldn't say anything about its momentum. Conversely, if you detect an electron's momentum, you won't be able to measure its position. In essence he was claiming that it

Above: Erwin Schrödinger's famous thought-experiment illustrates Heisenberg's uncertainty principle. A cat, a sealed vial of poison and a small lump of radioactive material are placed in a box. The vial will open if one atom in the radioactive material decays. Since no one can predict when this decay will occur, there is no way of knowing whether the cat is dead or alive. While the box remains closed, the cat is therefore in a 'superposition state', being both dead and alive.

was always impossible to predict what an electron would do next inside an atom, because of the uncertainty left when you try to measure it.

There are two ways of looking at this. One is to say that the experiments were just not sophisticated enough to do this, but give it a few years and someone would solve the problem. The other was to claim that this was a true reflection of a fundamental property of matter, one he said was described by quantum mechanics. Heisenberg presented this to Wolfgang Pauli in a fourteen-page letter in 1927 and then subsequently presented it to the world. Heisenberg's uncertainty principle had arrived.

Chien-Shiung Wu

The development of particle accelerators in the decades leading up to and including the 1950s allowed scientists to explore the previously unknown, small-scale world and discover a plethora of new particles. It was a period of searching for new particles while explaining how they behaved according to laws of physics. In this emerging field, Chien-Shiung Wu provided contradictory evidence to an assumed law of conservation, ultimately changing our understanding of how particles interact.

Born: 31 May 1912, Liuhe, China
Importance: Overturned conventional ideas about particle interaction
Died: 16 February 1997, New York City, United States

Every particle has several fundamental properties – charge, mass, spin and colour – and they can interact via the four fundamental forces: strong, weak, electromagnetic and gravitation.

Through these forces, particles can decay into other particles or bond to create new ones, but each interaction must obey the laws of physics. For example, the total electric charge before and after an electron interaction must be the same. This is called charge conservation.

In 1956, as scientists learned of the properties of these new fundamental particles, it was theorized that the universe would show no preference to a particle over its mirror image. That is to say, the number of particles and mirror-image particles would be the same for a given interaction.

Parity is the transformation of a particle by flipping it along an axis, creating the mirror image, much like reflecting a clock so the hands turn anti-clockwise. If there are even numbers of particles and mirror-image particles, the flipping of particles, or parity, must be showing no favouritism to particles over their mirror image. This is the theory of conservation of parity. At this time, many experiments had already shown this was true when particles interacted via the strong force and the electromagnetic force. By extension, it was theorized that particles interacting via the weak force would also follow this theory. Wu designed and conducted an experiment, the Wu Experiment, which ultimately disproved the conservation of parity as a universal theory.

After moving to the United States from Nanjing, China, Wu had spent years working on the emission of electrons from the nucleus of an atom, or beta decay, as well as contributing to the Manhattan Project. Using her incomparable experimental skills, Wu created an experiment with the ultimate goal of counting the number of particles and mirror-image particles in a specific interaction to check the conservation of parity via the weak interaction.

She used a radioactive isotope of cobalt, cobalt-60, cooled down to incredibly low temperatures just above absolute zero (around −273°C) inside a strong magnetic field. This ensured all the particles inside the nucleus of the cobalt-60 atoms had a spin in the same direction. As the cobalt-60 emitted electrons via beta decay, Wu counted the number of emitted electrons that had a spin in one direction, i.e. the particles, plus a spin in the other direction, i.e. the mirror-image particles. However, Wu observed a large difference in these numbers, proving that the parity was not conserved.

Since the revelation that parity is not conserved from Wu's experiments and work, new explanations for observed interactions have been developed and the Standard Model for particle physics has been updated to explain the results of the Wu Experiment. Parity still plays an important role in particle interactions but not the one we had previously assumed.

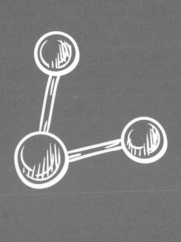

Chemistry

The popular image of the scientist
is of the white-coated eccentric,
tinkering away in a laboratory
full of bubbling chemicals. The
technology of chemistry has moved
on over the centuries but the basic
concept is still the same. In this
chapter, we read about some of the
greats, whose determination and,
sometimes, luck has elevated them
above their peers.

Chemical Nomenclature

The attempt of Lavoisier to reform chemical nomenclature
is premature. One single experiment may destroy the whole
filiation of his terms...
Thomas Jefferson

The system for the naming of chemical elements has changed
substantially in modern days. One of the earliest scientists
to name elements was Antoine Lavoisier (1743–1794) who
attempted to describe what each element does by their name.
Hydrogen, for example, means 'water-producing' and comes from
its ability to form water when combined with oxygen. Oxygen,
another Lavoisier name, means 'acid-producing', because he
believed it was the essential ingredient of acids – he was ultimately
wrong in this but the name stuck. Lavoisier also named carbon,
from the Latin for 'glowing coal'.

Sir William Ramsay (1852–1916) was another scientist
responsible for naming several elements in the same way,
including argon (meaning lazy or not working, as a result of its
inertness), xenon (meaning strange), and krypton (from hidden,
as it was so rare).

The modern system for naming elements came about
following a series of disputes over who first invented or discovered
something new. The controversy surrounding the naming of the
chemical element with atomic number 105 is a case in point.

Elements with high atomic numbers are inherently unstable
and not found in nature. As a result, they can only be 'discovered'
by creating them artificially in nuclear laboratories.

Two laboratories – the Joint Institute for Nuclear Research
at Dubna in the former Soviet Union and the Berkeley lab at the
University of California – believed they had discovered it and

suggested names. The Soviets wanted it to be called nielsbohrium, after Niels Bohr (1885–1962), while the Americans preferred hahnium, after the scientists Otto Hahn (1879–1968).

In an effort to keep the peace, the International Union of Pure and Applied Chemistry (IUPAC) – which is the body that officially sanctions element names – came up with a systematic naming scheme for elements with an atomic number greater than 100 that few could argue with.

Each digit in the element's atomic number is assigned a word root according to the following scheme:

0 = nil, 1 = un, 2 = bi, 3 = tri, 4 = quad, 5 = pent, 6 = hex, 7 = sept, 8 = oct, 9 = enn

The three roots are then strung together and the suffix – *ium* appended. Thus the atomic element 105 has the name unnilpentium. The chemical symbol is just the initial letters of the three roots, viz Unp.

In the end, unnilpentium got itself a so-called trivial name after all. In 1997, IUPAC ruled that the Soviet (by this time Russian) team had scientific priority. Rather than calling it by the previously disputed name of nielsbohrium IUPAC suggested dubnium after the location of the Russian lab.

The most recent names granted respectability by IUPAC are flerovium (Fl, 114) and livermorium (Lv, 116), both named after the nuclear laboratories where they were discovered: the Flerov Laboratory for Nuclear Reactions and the Lawrence Livermore National Laboratory.

Robert Boyle

Having space to research and develop new ideas is costly. You need either a wealthy benefactor or vast private sources of wealth. For Robert Boyle, it was inherited wealth that gave him the freedom to think.

Born: 1627, Lismore, Ireland
Importance: Identified the physical nature of gases
Died: 1691, London, England

Born in Lismore Castle in Munster, Ireland, Boyle grew to develop a passion for alchemy, a subject that, in the seventeenth century, was studied by a highly secretive international network of colourful characters who believed that through their studies they would find ways of generating gold from base materials and discover a mechanism or potion that would extend life.

In 1661 Boyle broke from the alchemist's obsession with secrecy and published *The Sceptical Chemist*, a book in which he criticised alchemists for the 'experiments whereby vulgar Spagyrists are wont to endeavour to evince their Salt, Sulphur and Mercury to be the true Principles of Things.'

In *The Sceptical Chemist*, Boyle presented the idea that matter consists of atoms and clusters of atoms. He suggested that these atoms moved around and collided with each other and that these collisions may cause new clusters, with new properties. Crucially he argued that the atoms making up the clusters hadn't changed. Indeed if you got the conditions right you could take these newly-created compounds and split them back into their original elements.

While Boyle was writing this book he had also been carrying out experiments with Robert Hooke (1635–1703). The experiments focused on the properties of air and were made possible because Hooke had developed a sophisticated air pump.

Working in Oxford, the pair had placed a lighted candle under a bell-jar and then pumped out the air. The flame was extinguished as a result. A burning coal in the airless bell-jar ceased to glow, but re-ignited if the air was returned before the coal cooled down. Clearly air was needed for items to burn. Using the same equipment, Boyle and Hooke found that air was also important for the transmission of sound. Through an ingenious set of devices, they managed to put a bell inside the jar, pumped out the air and then struck the bell. With no air in the jar, they couldn't hear the bell.

Making sense of all of this was difficult, but Boyle did sort out an intriguing relationship between volume and pressure. Boyle realised that to make discoveries you needed to control a situation carefully and change one thing at a time. In studying gas there are four variables that need considering: the amount of gas, its temperature, its pressure, and the volume of the container that is holding it. Boyle fixed the amount of gas and its temperature during his investigations, but varied the volume of the container or the pressure exerted on it. He found that when he halved the container's volume, the pressure of the gas doubled. If he decreased the surrounding pressure, the container's volume increased. We now know this relationship as Boyle's Law – for a fixed mass of gas, pressure and volume are inversely proportional. It formed the basis of all future work on the physical properties of gases.

Alchemy: The ancient predecessor of modern chemistry. The most well known goal of alchemy was the transmutation of any metal into either gold or silver. Alchemists also tried to create a panacea, a cure for all diseases and a way to prolong life indefinitely. A third goal of many alchemists was the creation of human life.

Antoine Lavoisier

In an attempt to explain fire, a substance known as phlogiston was conjured up by scientists in the mid 1600s. This combustible component was believed to be contained within all substances and objects that could burn. It took 18th-century French aristocrat Antoine-Laurent de Lavoisier to show that phlogiston was a flight of fancy and that it was the presence of oxygen that caused things to burn.

Born: 1743, Paris, France
Importance Naming the gases
Died: 1794, Paris, France

Educated at the French capital's prestigious Collège des Quatre-Nations, Lavoisier studied a wide range of subjects including astronomy, chemistry, mathematics and botany. By the age of 21, he had trained to become a lawyer but his career changed direction when he followed his passion for chemistry, which had become a hugely popular subject at the time because of the discoveries of the likes of chemist Joseph Priestley (1733–1804), who identified a gas that he called 'dephlogisticated' air, which Lavoisier would later name as oxygen.

Experimenting with combustion in an effort to discredit the phlogiston theory, Lavoisier created an experimental set-up in which objects could be burned and the resultant products weighed. In 1777, he published a paper entitled *Memoir on Combustion in General* based on these experiments. He noted that combustible items would only burn in a particular type of air – the 'dephlogisticated' air of Joseph Priestley – and that the fire would soon extinguish if placed in a vacuum.

Crucially, he also noted that the burning object increases in weight exactly in proportion to the quantity of pure air destroyed or decomposed – a hugely important principle of chemistry, that of mass conservation. Accordingly, he stated, 'the existence of the matter of fire, of phlogiston in metals, sulfur, etc., is then actually nothing but a hypothesis.'

He was also interested in the formation of acids and, in 1778, renamed Priestley's dephlogisticated air 'oxygen' – a name taken from Greek, meaning acid-forming and based on his view, later proven erroneous, that it was a necessary component of all acids. His naming of elements did not stop there. He named hydrogen in 1783 and also coined names for more than 30 other elements and substances, most of which are still in use today.

We must trust to nothing but facts: These are presented to us by Nature, and cannot deceive. We ought, in every instance, to submit our reasoning to the test of experiment.

Antoine Lavoisier

On Lavoisier's death (he was beheaded during the French Revolution), the mathematician Joseph-Louis Lagrange (1736–1813) remarked: 'It only took a moment to let his head fall; a hundred years may not be enough to make another like it.'

John Dalton

It is hard to imagine a world without the familiar concept of distinct elements made up of atoms with particular chemical properties, but it was not until a young Englishman called John Dalton, interested in the weather, turned his mind to creating an atomic theory of chemistry that the picture we know today emerged.

Born: 1766, Eaglesfield, England
Importance: Advanced our understanding of atomic theory
Died: 1844, Manchester, England

Born to a Quaker family, Dalton was a teacher for most of his life – in the fields of mathematics and natural philosophy. He had developed an early fascination with maths and meteorology under the guidance of Quaker meteorologist and instrument maker Elihu Robinson (1734–1809). Dalton's interest in the gases of the atmosphere led him to propose the law of partial pressures, now known as Dalton's Law. This states that the pressure exerted by each gas in a mixture is independent of the pressure exerted by the other gases, and that the total pressure is the sum of the pressures of each gas. He soon began to believe that the atoms of each of the gases had a fundamental nature that explained their chemical interactions.

This proposal of an atomic theory of chemistry was inspired in part by Antoine Lavoisier's (1743–1794) law of mass conservation and Joseph Louis Proust's (1754–1826) law of definite proportions, which states that when a compound is broken down into its constituents, the weights of those constituents are always in the same ratio, no matter how much of the original substance there is.

In 1803, Dalton published a table showing the relative atomic weights of six elements – hydrogen, oxygen, nitrogen, carbon, sulphur and phosphorus. He took as his base the element hydrogen, the lightest known, which was assigned a value of one.

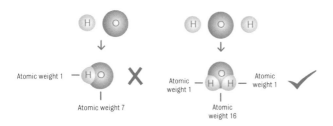

Above: To calculate the weight of a given atom, Dalton looked at molecules and tried to determine the mass of one atom (here, hydrogen) relative to another atom (oxygen). This meant determining the hydrogen-to-oxygen mass ratio in water, which he believed was 1:7. We know today that the combining ratio of hydrogen to oxygen atoms is 2:1. This means that the mass ratio is 1:8, or 2:16, so if we take the atomic weight of hydrogen to be 1, that of oxygen must be 16.

Rather than theorising about the inner subatomic structure, which would not be clear for another century, Dalton based his ideas on empirical observations, which is probably what drove him to list the atomic weight of oxygen as seven rather than eight as we know it today.

In a lecture to the Royal Institution of Great Britain the same year, Dalton went further and proposed a fully fledged atomic theory based on a number of key principles: all matter is composed of atoms, which cannot be made or destroyed; all atoms of the same element are identical; different elements have different types of atoms; chemical reactions occur when atoms are rearranged; and compounds are formed from atoms of the constituent elements.

Dalton incorrectly believed that a water molecule consisted of one hydrogen atom and one oxygen atom, or HO rather than the now familiar H_2O. Despite this, his theories stand the test of time.

Friedrich Wöhler

It is a tradition of science that before experimenting on others, it was the decent thing to carry out experiments on oneself. Many medical developments would never have happened without this simple precept. Friedrich Wöhler was one scientist to do this, and his paper on how waste products pass into urine, using both his own and that of his dogs as examples, is considered a classic of the genre.

Born: 1754, Como, Italy
Importance: Disproved the theory of vitalism which held that organic substances can only be produced by living things
Died: 1827, Como, Italy

Wöhler seemed destined for a career as a doctor, studying medicine at Heidelberg University and obtaining an MD in 1823. But while there he attended lectures by the chemist Leopold Gmelin (1788–1853) and was, in turn, encouraged to take up chemistry, for which he had a great aptitude. Gmelin was instrumental in getting Wöhler to spend a year with Swedish chemist Jöns Jakob Berzelius (1779–1848) in Stockholm, where Wöhler became a great experimentalist.

Wöhler's greatest contribution to science, made when he returned from Sweden to Germany, is best put in the words that he himself wrote: 'I can no longer, as it were, hold back my chemical urine; and I have to let out that I can make urea without needing a kidney, whether of man or dog.' What he meant by this was that he

> This investigation has yielded an unanticipated result that reaction of cyanic acid with ammonia gives urea, a noteworthy result in as much as it provides an example of the artificial production of an organic, indeed a so-called animal, substance from inorganic substances.
>
> Friedrich Wöhler

$CO(NH_2)_2$

Above: Later named the Wöhler synthesis, Wöhler's reaction of cyanic acid and ammonium to produce urea was the first time an organic compound had been created outside a living organism, without needing the kidney of either a human or a dog.

had worked out how to synthesise urea by reacting lead cyanate and ammonium hydroxide with each other. It was the first time that someone had managed to create a natural product outside a living organism. This discovery also demonstrated the concept of isomerism – the idea that two distinct compounds could have the same chemical formula.

Wöhler also made great advances in the isolation of several metals, notably boron, silicon, beryllium, titanium and, particularly, aluminium. Many great chemists, including his mentor Berzelius and the great Humphrey Davy (1778–1829), had tried to isolate aluminium without success. Wöhler's treatment of anhydrous aluminium chloride with a potassium amalgam therefore succeeded where these others had failed.

Yet it was his synthesis of urea that was to secure his place in history. The discovery of this creation process is considered so vital that it is often said to be the moment that the discipline of organic chemistry – the chemistry of carbon-containing substances – began.

Dmitry Mendeleyev

Born in the Siberian town of Tobolsk in 1834, Mendeleyev made his most important contribution to chemistry when he was 35 and a teacher at St Petersburg University. By the time Dmitry Mendeleyev came to do this work, chemistry had moved a long way forward from the days of the 17th-century alchemists who believed that materials could be transformed from one to another.

Born: 1834, Tobolsk, Siberia, Russia
Importance: Drew up the first periodic table
Died: 1907, St Petersburg, Russia

Now chemists were aware that at a chemical level, materials were built of unchanging elements, and these elements combined to make molecules. One question started rising to the top of chemists' minds: why did different materials sometimes look and behave alike?

As a youngster Mendeleyev had moved to St Petersburg from Siberia after his father died and the family needed to find work. He was the youngest of 14 children, but worked hard and eventually became a teacher at the University of St Petersburg and subsequently the Professor of Chemistry. Here he set about looking at similarities in the behaviours of different elements.

According to Mendeleyev's notes, his periodic table came as a spark of inspiration while he was setting out to write a new chemistry textbook. In a remarkably creative few hours on 17 February 1869, Mendeleyev sat down with 63 cards. On each card he wrote the name of one element, its atomic weight and physical and chemical properties. This pack contained all of the elements known at that time.

By sorting the cards in a grid-like pattern, Mendeleyev realised that you could place them so that the atomic weight increased as you went down a column, but elements in any row shared similar properties. The first column started with lithium, followed

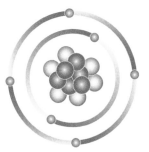

Left: Mendeleyev arranged elements according to their reactive properties and the number of protons in their nucleus. Niels Bohr's subsequent work developed the idea that different elements also have different numbers of electrons 'orbiting' the central nucleus, as in this diagram of a carbon atom.

Atomic weight: The relative mass of an atom of an element compared to the mass of carbon-12.

by beryllium, boron, carbon, nitrogen, oxygen, and fluorine. In a modern periodic table the grid has been turned sideways and this set of elements appears as the first row. Mendeleyev decided to leave gaps in the table, guessing – correctly – that some elements were yet to be discovered. Equally he grouped some elements according to their properties, even though the weights didn't fit the pattern. He rightly assumed that the recorded weights were wrong. Over time, as the missing elements were found and the weights were recorded accurately, chemists discovered that they matched Mendeleyev's predictions. Designing a system for explaining what you know is clever. Using that explanation to make accurate predictions is remarkable.

It took another half century before the rationale underlying Mendeleyev's observational work gained a foundation in the work of Niels Bohr (1885–1962), whose concept of 'orbits' showed that different elements have different numbers of electrons 'orbiting' the central nucleus.

Emil Fischer

Emil Fischer was a brilliant chemist, correctly detailing the structure of many key organic substances before going on to create many of these in the lab for the first time ever. He is best known for his work on sugars, such as fructose and glucose.

Born: 1852, Euskirchen, Germany
Importance: Unlocking the chemistry of sugar
Died: 1919, Berlin, Germany

Originally destined to follow his father into the lumber trade, Fischer was instead convinced by his cousin Otto to study chemistry, first at the University of Bonn and then at Strasbourg under the eminent professor Adolf von Baeyer (1835–1917). Fischer worked with von Baeyer and eventually synthesised a substance called phenylhydrazine, used in the dye and pharmaceutical industries, which set him on a bright career in organic chemistry.

It was at Erlangen, where he moved to in 1881, that he did his most famous work. He began by analysing the chief organic compounds in tea and coffee, particularly caffeine and theobromine, and worked out how to produce them synthetically. Extending his work to compounds found in animal excreta, including uric acid and guanine, as well as adenine, he began to realise that they all – including caffeine – belonged to a single family of compounds, which he called the purines.

> Once a molecule is asymmetric, its extension proceeds also in an asymmetrical sense.
> This concept completely eliminates the difference between natural and artificial synthesis. The advance of science has removed the last chemical hiding place for the once so highly esteemed *vis vitalis*.
>
> Emil Fischer

In 1885, Fischer left von Baeyer's laboratory for the University of Würzburg where he changed the direction of his research for the next decade to concentrate on the organic chemistry of sugars. He worked in the same methodical way as before, watching how these compounds reacted and how they degraded before suggesting their stereochemistry, or three-dimensional structure. (In so doing, he developed the Fischer projection method, still used today, which allows chemists to represent three-dimensional shapes on a sheet of paper.)

He then moved on to synthesising the compounds. In 1890, he suggested how the sugars glucose and fructose are related and succeeded in synthesising both – an important breakthrough in that it was the first step in the artificial production of complex sugars that are rare in nature.

Fischer also did much pioneering work on proteins and enzymes, suggesting the method of operation of the latter was analogous to a lock and key. This analogy has been vital in understanding how to develop enzymes that can treat disease or manipulate genes. Fischer's own work was like one of these enzymes, unlocking the mysteries of organic chemistry.

Paul Ehrlich

An early pioneer of the use of chemistry in medicine, Paul Ehrlich was hugely influential in the development of 'blockbuster' drugs. His concept of 'magic bullets' – his term for synthetic chemicals – binding to receptors of a target disease and destroying it, was groundbreaking and remains central to the pharmaceutical industry today.

Born: 1854, Strehlen, Germany
Importance: Discovered the earliest drugs of the modern era
Died: 1915, Bad Homberg, Germany

Ehrlich gained a doctorate of medicine in 1878 and began researching the use of dyes for staining tissue specimens. He found the dyes allowed for more detailed work to be done under the microscope and classified his dyes into three groups: basic, acid or neutral. His work on staining structures within blood cells formed the basis of modern haematology. In 1875, he described mast cells, key players in the immune system, for the first time.

In 1882 Ehrlich published a method of staining the tuberculosis bacillus still used today, albeit in modified form. This also forms the basis of the Gram method of staining, used in the classification of bacteria. From 1890, he carried out work on immunology with Robert Koch (1843–1910) at the new Institute of Infectious Diseases, investigating serum, antibodies and the toxins produced by certain bacteria. He developed an antitoxin for use against diphtheria, and, with Russian bacteriologist Elie Metchnikoff (1845–1916), received the Nobel Prize for Physiology or Medicine in 1908, in recognition of their advances in the science and understanding of immunology.

In 1899, Ehrlich became Director of the new Royal Institute of Experimental Therapy in Frankfurt. He turned his attention to chemotherapy, developing ideas about how the chemical structure of drugs related to their mode of action in the cell and their affinity for cell components. He formulated his 'side chain theory', explaining how specific dyes bound chemically to specific locations within the cell (side chains) and how antibodies, similarly, could bind to antigens. In 1900, he and his assistant, Julius Morgenroth (1871–1924), renamed the side chains 'receptors'. Ehrlich began researching synthetic chemicals (his magic bullets) that would bind to receptors on a disease target – whether a cancer cell, inflammatory molecule, virus or bacterium – and so destroy (or at least neutralise) it.

He began testing hundreds of substances for magic-bullet properties and found a dye, Trypan Red, which was active against trypanosome parasites. He began work on syphilis, which was caused by the newly discovered spirochaete bacterium *Treponema pallidum* and tested many different arsenic compounds. His assistant, Sahachiro Hata (1873–1938), discovered that compound number 606 worked against syphilis in rabbits and, later, in humans. Its introduction, in 1910, under the name Salvarsan, was the first treatment for syphilis, although it was not a very good drug – it was unstable and had to be injected. In 1912 an improved version, Neosalvarsan was introduced. Chemotherapy did not really gain acceptance until the large-scale production of penicillin during World War II, when it was shown to be effective against syphilis.

> Substances created in the chemist's retort will be able to exert their full action exclusively on the parasite harboured within the organism and would represent, so to speak, magic bullets which seek their target of their own accord.
>
> Paul Ehrlich

Irène Joliot-Curie

Having two Nobel laureates as parents would put strain on any child, but the daughter of Marie and Pierre Curie achieved her own scientific success. By converting one element into another, she realised an ancient dream, improved radiomedicine and earned her own Nobel Prize.

Born: 1897, Paris, France
Importance: Pioneered the artificial creation of radioactive elements
Died: 1956, Paris, France

Before modern chemistry, there was alchemy. Humans mixed, burned and distilled substances for centuries in pursuit of alchemical dreams – an elixir of life, or a philosopher's stone. An obsession with the later object, which was supposed to turn 'base matter' into gold, occupied great minds including Isaac Newton (1643–1727).

Irène Joliot-Curie, along with her husband, actually did turn one element into another. She converted boron into nitrogen, aluminium into phosphorus, and magnesium into silicon by bombarding these elements with radioactive particles. Her parents, Marie and Pierre Curie, had helped discover the existence of radioactivity while Irène was a child.

Irène was born in Paris in 1897. By then her parents were both practising chemists, though they performed their research in a converted shed on the campus of one of the city's Grandes Écoles. Marie and Pierre would discover and name the elements radium and polonium in that shed before Irène turned three.

In 1925, Irène completed her doctorate by studying the radioactive decay of polonium at the Radium Institute, a school built by her parents. There she trained a young scientist named Frédéric Joliot (1900–1958). The two soon married and would study chemistry together for the rest of their short lives.

Almost every chemical element is stable, meaning it will not change into another element once isolated. Naturally radioactive elements like those that Marie and Pierre helped discover are the exception. Radio-elements decay at a definite rate. Radium, for example, eventually turns into the element radon via emission of an alpha particle. This happens because the radium nucleus is inherently unstable.

Irène and Frédéric discovered that some the so-called stable elements – including aluminium, boron and magnesium – can be transmuted too if they are bombarded with alpha particles. In the case of aluminium, this transformation involves the absorption of an alpha particle into the nucleus, creating a new, unstable isotope of phosphorus which eventually decays into the stable element silicon. Irène and Frédéric discovered this process by placing radioactive polonium near aluminum foil. They were jointly awarded the Nobel Prize in Chemistry in 1935 for this research.

Creating new radioactive elements proved tremendously useful. Targeted radiotherapy as a treatment for cancer was already in use at the time, but the Joliot-Curies' discovery that new radio-elements could be manufactured made such therapies much cheaper and more widely available, eventually saving millions of lives.

Linus Pauling

Winning a Nobel Prize is surely the pinnacle of any scientist's career. Given the nature of scientific research, the likelihood of winning one unshared with others is becoming increasingly remote. This makes Linus Pauling's achievement of winning two unshared Nobel Prizes – one for chemistry and one for peace – even more remarkable.

Born: 1901, Portland, Oregon
Importance: Explaining the carbon bond
Died: 1923, Munich, Germany

Pauling's achievement is less surprising when you consider his wide-ranging interests: he published hundreds of scientific papers on a bewildering range of subjects, from X-ray diffraction and the structure of metals, to proteins, antibodies, and hemoglobin.

However, it is as a result of his work on the nature of chemical bonds that he has secured his place in the history of science. His insight was to combine the then new theories of quantum mechanics with the shared electron theory of chemical binding. In particular, in 1932, he suggested how quantum mechanics could explain the challenge posed by carbon; physicists said it should form two strong bonds while chemists knew that it made four, making the classic tetrahedron shape. Pauling's breakthrough came when he worked out how to use the wave functions of quantum mechanics to describe the probabilities of where these four electrons would be in their orbits; his calculations showed that carbon should have a natural tetrahedral shape.

> Even the formal justification of the electron-pair bond in the simplest cases...requires a formidable array of symbols and equations.
>
> Linus Pauling

Above: Pauling confirmed that carbon has a natural tetrahedral shape, as shown on the left. Carbon forms four covalent bonds, which means it has the ability to form giant covalent structures, such as diamond, shown on the right. Here the tetrahedral shape becomes a rigid lattice arrangement.

In 1939, Pauling published what was to become one of the most influential chemistry books of all time: *The Nature of the Chemical Bond and the Structure of Molecules and Crystals.* Although this book dealt with a weighty subject – how quantum mechanics governed the behavior of molecules and compounds – it was written in a way that was accessible to undergraduates, leading to it becoming a standard textbook.

In 1954, he was awarded the Nobel Prize for chemistry. It was then Pauling's unstinting opposition to the bombs that had ended World War II and initiated the Cold War that won him his second Nobel Prize eight years later.

Pauling is also at least partly responsible for the notion that vitamin C is effective in preventing and reducing the severity of the common cold and of preventing cancer, although its efficacy is strongly debated even today.

Dorothy Crowfoot Hodgkin

Throughout the fields of chemistry and biochemistry, the overall shape of a molecule is known to influence its function, but to know its shape, you need to know its structure – you need to know how the atoms are arranged.

Born: 1910, Cairo, Egypt
Importance: Pioneered
X-ray crystallography
Died: 1994, Shipston-on-
Stour, England

In the latter part of the 19th century, chemists started calculating the shapes of some of the large, carbon-containing compounds that are fundamental to life. They made assumptions about what bonds would form and built scale models to describe the compound structures. Although the exercise worked reasonably well with small molecules, it failed with the larger ones.

In the first years of the 20th century scientists began to realise that, when they shone X-rays through crystals and onto photosensitive paper, they got patterns. The idea is that when X-rays hit a crystal, the electrons surrounding each atom bend the beam. Because there are many atoms arranged in repeating patterns within the crystal, the X-rays produce a series of light and dark patches. Measuring the intensity and relative position of each patch gives clues about the relative positions of atoms within the crystal. Now people could start to make sense of the three-dimensional structure of compounds.

The problem was that some of the most useful – and therefore most valuable – compounds were highly complex, with each molecule containing many hundreds of atoms, each held in a precise location.

Born in Cairo, Egypt, and educated at Oxford University, Crowfoot moved to work with John Desmond Bernal (1901–1971) in Cambridge and started to develop techniques of X-ray crystallography. One of her early successes was making predictions about the structure of a small protein called pepsin. After making huge progress in determining how to use X-ray diffraction,

Crowfoot moved to Oxford in 1933, and started work on insulin, a task that took her 34 years to complete. During this time she married in 1937 and became Dorothy Crowfoot Hodgkin.

In the 1930s and 1940s the germ-busting antibiotic penicillin arrived on the scene. Initial clinical hopes for this drug were dashed because it was difficult to harvest from microbes, and there was no hope of manufacturing it until someone could work out its structure. Hodgkin turned her X-rays on it and found that it had an unusual ring feature, now known as the Beta-lactam structure. This discovery started to give important clues about how the antibiotic worked. In 1955 she took the first X-ray diffraction photos of vitamin B_{12}.

With this pioneering work in X-ray crystallography, Hodgkin was able to discover the chemical structure of penicillin, vitamin B_{12} and insulin, which enabled them to be manufactured synthetically and become widely available to those in need.

She showed us that we could look inside molecules and see their structure. From here it is a short step to predict their function and work out how to design chemical drugs that could affect them. Biochemistry and the pharmaceutical industry would never be the same again.

> I became captivated by the edifices chemists had raised through experiment and imagination – but still I had a lurking question. Would it not be better if one could really 'see' whether molecules as complicated as the sterols, or strychnine were just as experiment suggested?
>
> Dorothy Crowfoot Hodgkin

Frederick Sanger

Winning one Nobel prize is a rare feat, but to receive two is truly special. Frederick Sanger got his first for showing how amino acids link together to form the protein insulin, and his second for developing a method of sorting out the sequence of molecular 'letters' that make up a genetic code.

Born: 1918, Rendcombe, England
Importance: Showed how amino acids link to form proteins, and how to read genetic codes
Died: 2013, Cambridge, England

Born the son of a medical practitioner, Sanger initially planned to become a doctor, but before going to university had decided to study science. Arriving at the University of Cambridge he gravitated rapidly to biochemistry and soon joined a team looking at the structure of proteins.

Initially Sanger turned his attention to insulin, the protein involved in diabetes. At the start of his work it was possible to look at the protein using an electron microscope and see its overall shape, or to mash it up chemically into a soup of 22 building blocks called 'amino acids'. Scientists knew that these amino acids were normally linked together in a long chain, but had no clue about the sequence of amino acids within the chain.

Sanger marked the end of the protein chain with a dye that grabbed hold of the last amino acid so strongly that it stuck there even when the chain was dismantled. By studying the amino acid linked to the dye he could say which one was at the beginning of the chain. He then developed a way of breaking the chain into lengths of two, three, four, five or more amino acids, and identified the amino acid at the end of each fragment. By doing this enough times he determined the order of 51 amino acids in a molecule of insulin. The same method could then be used to analyse any other protein of interest.

His second breakthough came when studying another chain-like structure, deoxyribonucleic acid – DNA. This time he wanted to determine the sequence of its 'bases', the building blocks from which it is made. The importance of this was that by now, scientists had realised that this sequence spells out the genetic instructions that make up our bodies. To an extent this task was simpler than for proteins, because DNA has only four different bases. But in fact the challenge was greater, because there were many thousands of bases in each sequence.

DNA code is written in four letters, A, C, T and G. The meaning lies in the sequence of the letters – the groups of three the letters fall into. Most groups of three letters code for an amino acid and some code for where the groups start and stop. For instance, the DNA letters TGC code for the amino acid cysteine, whereas the DNA letters TGG code for amino acid tryptophan. Each of these sequences of three is called a DNA triplet, or codon. The codons that don't code for amino acids provide the grammar of the DNA sequence. For instance, the codon TAA means 'stop', essential for telling the cell when to halt producing proteins.

Molecule: A collection of two or more atoms held together by chemical bonds.

Amino Acids: The building blocks of proteins; the main material of the body's cells. Insulin is made of 51 amino acids joined together.

Again Sanger generated fragments of the sequence, this time ending at each different base. By measuring the length of each fragment he showed that you could determine the complete sequence. The process readily lends itself to computer automation, which has allowed scientists to tackle huge sequences, including the three-billion-base sequence that makes up the human genome – the DNA inside the nucleus of each human cell. Genetics had come of age.

Stephanie Kwolek

Kevlar is one of the most versatile polymers due to its incredible strength and light weight. Stephanie Kwolek, a materials scientist working at the American chemicals company DuPont, invented this incredible polymer in the 1960s by taking a chance on an odd new mixture and trusting her gut. Today, Kevlar is widely used in hundreds of different applications including saving lives as the main material in bulletproof vests.

Born: 1923, Pennsylvania, USA
Importance: Invented the first of an exceptional family of synthetic fibres
Died: 2014, Delware, USA

After the discovery of nylon in the 1930s and the end of the Second World War, there was a large push in the field of materials science to invent more synthetic fibres and polymers that could be used in a range of areas. These synthetic fibres are made up almost exclusively of one repeating structure, a monomer, joined together to create long chains or large configurations.

In the 1960s many had predicted a shortage of petrol that would lead to a skyrocket in prices, so Kwolek began working for DuPont as a chemist tasked with creating a new fibre with incredible strength and stiffness in order to increase the efficiency of car tyres and reduce the consumption of petrol.

To create these synthetic fibres a solution made of the newly created polymer solution is spun into long strands. This solution was usually clear and quite thick. However, in 1965, Kwolek, produced a milky, runny solution. Typically, such a solution would have been discarded but Kwolek decided to test it out regardless.

After convincing everyone this solution was worth spinning into a fibre, Kwolek ran the usual tests to determine the characteristics of the new fibre. She found this new material, eventually named Kevlar, had incredible strength five times greater than steel while maintaining a light weight.

Kwolek determined that the secret to the incredible strength of Kevlar was also the cause of the milky colour of the solution. Under certain reaction conditions, the polymers would join together to create long rod-like crystals. When spun to create the fibre, these crystal rods line up in parallel, dramatically increasing the overall combined strength.

While Kevlar was introduced to make tyres stronger and stiffer, it currently has hundreds of other applications. The spun fibres are woven into fabrics to provide unprecedented strength, creating bullet proof vests, gloves, boots and helmets for protection. It is also used in many sporting industries, from sails to basketball shoes, ropes for mooring and tennis rackets. It is even used for fibre optics.

Kwolek's perseverance as a materials scientist led to her invention of a versatile and vital fibre. Scientists are still learning new useful properties of Kevlar and controlling the reaction to create versions of Kevlar with specific properties for each purpose. Kevlar is now a ubiquitous product in many fields and it has changed the way we live, while also saving countless lives.

Frances Arnold

Sometimes it takes an outsider to see what other scientists have overlooked. Frances Arnold's pioneering work on 'directed evolution' won her half of the 2018 Nobel Prize in Chemistry.

Born: 1956, Pennsylvania, USA
Importance: Pioneered the use of directed evolution to engineer enzymes

Before Arnold came along, evolution was something biologists studied, not something they used. Charles Darwin (1809–1882) and others famously discovered that mutation followed by natural selection is the primary force that gives shape to the living world. Since Darwin's day, geneticists, palaeontologists, ecologists and microbiologists have studied how this process happens.

Arnold was none of these. A mechanical engineer by training, Arnold came to see evolution the way a builder might: as a tool for making things. In the early 1990s, she stopped trying to rationally design better enzymes – the catalysts of biology – and instead tried evolving them. This meant intentionally making mutations to enzymes in a laboratory, then artificially selecting versions that performed their chemical transformation more efficiently. Using this technique, Arnold and others have created new enzymes that produce fuels, medicines and precursors to plastics, among other things.

Early in her career, Arnold researched renewable energy. After graduating from Princeton in 1979, she worked as a solar power engineer in South Korea, Brazil and the United States before completing her PhD in chemical engineering at the University of California, Berkeley in 1985. There she developed a deep appreciation for the way biomolecules operate, and decided she would apply her engineering skills to the challenge of enzyme design.

Enzymes, which contain thousands of interacting atoms, are too complex for chemical engineers to rationally modify in most cases. Arnold's insight was to abandon 'rational design' in favour of an alternative strategy: random mutation followed by selection. Arnold, who is now the Linus Pauling Professor of Chemical Engineering, Bioengineering and Biochemistry at the California Institute for Technology, was initially ridiculed for her new 'directed evolution' technique. Many scientists thought it unseemly, neither proper nor rigorous enough to be called true science. But Arnold was undeterred. She understood that evolution was 'nature's design process', and that when it came to engineering complex biomolecules such as enzymes, no other other strategy yet worked.

> What I do is copying nature's design process. All this tremendous beauty and complexity of the biological world all comes about through this one simple, beautiful design algorithm, and what I do is use that algorithm to build new biological things.
>
> Frances Arnold

Scores of other scientists now use Arnold's technique, and she continues to produce new enzymes using directed evolution to this day. In addition to winning a Nobel Prize, Arnold was the first woman elected to all three National Academies in the United States – the National Academy of Engineering, the National Academy of Medicine and the National Academy of Sciences.

Andre Geim

Scientists often start working in a field for their PhD and pursue the same subject until they retire; not so the Russian-born Andre Geim, who said, 'I have changed my subject five times before I got my first tenured position'. Geim has achieved outstanding success in all these fields – and two of his papers are among the 100 most cited research papers in scientific history – but he is best known for the discovery of graphene.

Born: 21 October 1958, Sochi, Russia

Importance: Discovered graphene, a material with many potential implications for the twenty-first century

Geim grew up in southern Russia, in the foothills of the Caucasus, and studied at the Russian Academy of Sciences. He worked as a researcher in microelectronics before moving to the UK in 1990 and deciding to leave his homeland behind – in the West he could pursue research rather than 'swimming through Soviet treacle'. While working in Nijmegen, in the Netherlands, he supervised work by Konstantin Novoselov (1974–), who went on to become his main research partner.

At the University of Manchester Geim and Novoselov pioneered a method for isolating layers of graphite a single atom thick. The results were published in 2004 and it was for this work that they were awarded the Nobel Prize for Physics in 2010. Scientists had long theorised about the existence of graphene, and very thin layers of graphite, consisting possibly of single atoms, had in fact been observed under electron microscopes. But the first method to extract graphene from graphite was devised by Geim and Novoselov in 2004.

In their lab they often held 'Friday night experiments' – playful sessions exploring unconventional methods not necessarily related to their everyday work. One Friday they removed flakes from a lump of graphite with a sticky tape. By repeatedly separating the flakes in this way, they were able to create layers a single atom thick. The carbon atoms in graphene form a honeycomb lattice that is one of the hardest and strongest materials ever tested, as well as the thinnest.

It is lightweight, flexible and transparent, yet many times stronger than steel. The material has endless potential applications, especially for energy storage in supercapacitors but also for touchscreen technology and biomedical science. Since the publication of Geim and Novoselov's discovery in 2004, Manchester has become a global hub for materials research developing new uses for graphene.

Beyond graphene, Geim's work includes the development of an adhesive tape known as gecko tape (because it is made from synthetic setae, the bristle-like hairs on geckos' feet that enable them to cling to almost any surface). In 2000, during an experiment with diamagnetic levitation, Geim used magnets to levitate a frog – a feat for which he won the Ig Nobel Prize. A decade later Geim became the first individual to win both the Nobel and Ig Nobel awards. He has since claimed to be proud of both, as the Ig Nobel 'was the manifestation that I can take jokes, a little bit of self-deprecation always helps'.

> **Diamagnetism:**
> The property of a very weakly magnetic substance – such as water or wood – to repel and be repelled by a strong magnetic field.

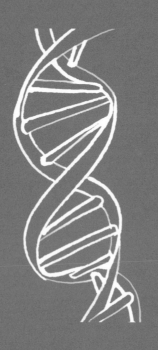

Genetics and Microbiology

The biological domain of the very
small is a recent development in
the history of science, but the
discoveries made by the scientists
studying microbiology and genetics
have led to some of the greatest
advances in human health as well
as giving us a better understanding
of life itself.

Evolution

We can allow satellites, planets, suns, universe, nay whole
systems of universes, to be governed by laws, but the
smallest insect, we wish to be created at once by special act.

Charles Darwin

Charles Darwin's celebrated publication of On the Origin of Species
forms just one step in a chain of events marking humanity's
struggle to make sense of the biological world.

In ancient Greece, Aristotle (384–322 BC) and his student
Theophrastus (later known as the father of botany) realized that
they could place plants and animals into groups by comparing
their physical features. This accompanied a realization that, on
the whole, plants and animals could only produce offspring if they
bred with other highly similar individuals – in other words, other
members of the same species.

For over 2,000 years the reason for this seemed obvious. God,
or some creative influence, had generated all the species found
on Earth and had made biological boundaries that ensured that
species didn't get mixed up.

By the time that Charles Darwin (1809–1882) stepped aboard
HMS Beagle and headed west to explore South America and the
Galapagos Islands in the Pacific Ocean, people were already
beginning to question this static idea of biological existence.
Charles Lyell (1779–1875) had begun to show that looking
at the structure of the Earth indicated that it may have existed
for millions of years. This alone sparked questions of whether
anything had changed significantly over that time.

On 24 November 1859, when Darwin eventually published
his book, science took a massive step into the unknown – but
a step that now underlies much of current biological thinking.

The full title of his book reads *On the Origin of Species by Means of Natural Selection, or the Preservation of Favoured Races in the Struggle for Life*. In it he shows how studying a wide range of plants and animals, as well as the environments they were found in, led him to conclude that animals which are best fitted to their environment are most likely to breed and pass on their characteristics to the next generation. Over enough time, he suggested, this process of gradual persistent change could generate individuals that were so different from their ancestors that they could no longer breed with non-changed members of the species. In other words, they developed to such an extent that they constituted a new species.

At the time Darwin was working, no one knew about DNA or genes and so the mechanism that allowed this passage of information from one generation to the next was a mystery. Austrian monk Gregor Mendel, however, was in the process of working out that physical characteristics were passed on in discrete units of information – what would become known as 'genes' – and was making distinct progress in determining some of the mathematical and statistical rules that describe the way this happens.

The arrival of genetic technology now reveals more details of the underlying mechanisms. The discovery that most living organisms share similar basic house-keeping genes points to a common ancestry, and analysis of the differences within these genes gives an indication of what species have evolved from each other. Darwin would be fascinated.

Edward Jenner

Smallpox was a hugely destructive disease that spread rapidly and killed a third of the people who caught it. Smallpox infection was characterized by fever, aches, and sometimes vomiting. This was followed by a rash, which marked the most contagious period, that progressed to raised bumps and severe blisters. These blisters would scab and fall off after about three weeks, leaving a pitted scar. Many survivors were scarred for life. Physician Edward Jenner found a solution to this feared killer.

Born: 1749, Berkeley, England
Importance: Discovered vaccination
Died: 1823, Berkeley, England

In the 18th century no one knew that bacteria or viruses existed, but they did know about smallpox. This disease gave influenza-like symptoms, followed by a rash all over an infected person's body. The rash developed into pus-filled blisters, and people tended to get infections in the kidneys and lungs before they died.

The only known way of becoming immune was to catch smallpox and survive. In China, doctors deliberately gave people small doses of the disease by grinding smallpox scabs or fleas that had fed on cows with cowpox, and blowing some of the dust into their nostrils. The hope was that they would only have a small bout of illness.

The idea slowly spread west. In the early 1700s English aristocrat Lady Mary Wortley Montague came back from a trip to Turkey having seen women in the Ottoman court making small graze marks on children's arms and wiping the area with smallpox scabs. The children became immune to the disease. Impressed with the idea, she had her five-year-old son treated in Turkey, and on returning to England, she got a surgeon to do the same to her four-year-old daughter.

Although the technique was fairly successful, it wasn't perfect. One in 50 people died as a result of such treatment, and it occasionally triggered smallpox outbreaks.

According to folklore, milkmaids who caught cowpox didn't get smallpox, and on 14 May 1796 Edward Jenner performed a vital, if terribly risky, experiment. He made two half-inch scratches on the arm of an eight-year-old boy and wiped a cowpox scab over the wound. The scab had originally come from the hands of a local milkmaid, Sarah Nelmes. Six weeks later, Jenner exposed the boy to smallpox. He did not become ill.

Virus: Ultra-microscopic infectious agent that replicates itself only within cells of living hosts.

The process worked for both the Chinese and for Jenner because the viruses causing cowpox and smallpox are remarkably similar. When exposed to cowpox viruses the person's immune system developed molecules that are ready and waiting to fight the virus. These same molecules, however, were equally capable of fighting smallpox viruses, so the person developed resistance to both diseases. Vaccination had arrived, and our language still remembers the event: the word 'vaccinate' comes from the Latin *vacca*, meaning 'cow'.

By 1800 some 100,000 people throughout the world had been vaccinated against smallpox, and in the 20th century the World Health Organisation made a concerted effort to wipe out the disease. On 27 October, 1977, Ali Maow Maalin, a 23-year-old hospital cook in a small Somali village called Merka, became the last person to catch smallpox in the wild. For the rest of the world, smallpox had been consigned to history.

Charles Darwin

When Charles Darwin concluded that new species had evolved from older ones by a process of natural selection, he created the theory of evolution and turned the world of biology, and in some ways theology, on its head.

Born: 1809, Shrewsbury, England
Importance: Theory of evolution
Died: 1882, Downe, England

While studying at the University of Cambridge, Charles Darwin went on various field trips to examine geological formations and their fossils. He started to question whether, for example, birds had wings because a creator God wanted them to fly, or whether birds could fly *because* they had wings.

Darwin's big break came in 1831 when he set sail on *HMS Beagle* as the companion of the ship's 26-year-old captain Robert FitzRoy (1805–1865). On the voyage they visited the Cape Verde Islands, the South American coast, the Strait of Magellan, the Galapagos Islands, Tahiti, New Zealand, Australia, the Maldives and Mauritius, before returning to England in 1833.

While travelling, Darwin read Charles Lyell's (1797–1875) *Principles of Geology*, which argued that the world was continually being shaped and reshaped by ongoing geological forces. This ran against the accepted view that the world had been created a long time ago, and had only changed occasionally as a result of major natural events such as catastrophic floods.

Arriving in South America, Darwin found fossil evidence that seemed to indicate some form of progression from simple to complex life forms. In addition, on 20 February, 1835, Darwin experienced an earthquake on the south-west coast of South America, which lifted the land by between one and three metres. Later he found fossilized seashells high up in the mountains and wondered whether numerous previous quakes

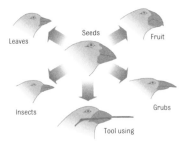

Left: On his groundbreaking trip to the Galapagos Islands, Darwin observed how the beaks of different species of finches were highly specialised depending on the food available on each island – a result, he argued, of natural selection.

Leaves

Seeds

Fruit

Insects

Grubs

Tool using

had driven them there. If so, this would support Lyell's theory that the earth was changing constantly.

From September to October 1835 Darwin visited the Galapagos Islands in the Pacific Ocean, which as far as he could see had been recently created by volcanic action. He was therefore surprised by the diversity of life that he found on the islands. On James Island he found 71 species of plant – of which 30 were unique to the island – and a further eight that were found only on other islands in this group. He was especially intrigued by the variety of species of finches, each with differently shaped beaks that seemed well suited to the particular food available on each island.

It turns out that Darwin wasn't alone in concluding that different species developed through a gradual process of evolution. Another explorer, Alfred Wallace (1823–1913) was studying hard in the Far East and had amassed over 125,000 specimens. Wallace sent a couple of letters to England outlining his ideas and, spurred on by this, Darwin quickly presented his theory to the Linnean Society of London on 1 July 1858. Just over a year later he published *On the Origin of Species*, one of the most influential books in the history of science.

Rudolf Virchow

Suspicious of the 'germ theory' put forward by his contemporary Louis Pasteur (1822–1895), Rudolf Virchow believed that disease came from within the body and not from external, infectious agents. In 1858, he published a book on cellular pathology in which he claimed that the cell was the basic unit of life, capable of reproducing itself. A radical view for its time, going against the popular view that life somehow arose spontaneously, this idea was nevertheless soon supported by Pasteur's experiments on microbes.

Born: 1821, Schivelbein, Pomerania (now Germany)
Importance: Founded the science of cellular pathology
Died: 1902, Berlin, Germany

Virchow studied medicine in Berlin, graduating in 1842, and gained a junior post at the city's leading hospital, the Charité. However, he lost his job in 1848, owing to his liberal political views. He subsequently moved to the city of Würzburg, where he became Professor of Pathological Anatomy. In 1856, he returned to Berlin to take up a post created for him at the newly established pathology institute at the university there. Virchow was also involved in the Franco-German war, when he led the first hospital train to the front line to help wounded soldiers.

Using developments in microscopy – such as the development of stains for tissues and cells, and the microtome, which cuts very thin slices of tissue for study – Virchow promoted the use of the microscope to advance the study of pathology. He described leukaemia, a group of blood cancers, in 1845, and was also one of the first to study inflammation, embolism and thrombosis (the last two being abnormal formations of blood clots) at the cellular level. He was the first to put forward the idea that a venous thrombosis in the leg could break off and travel to the lung, forming a potentially fatal embolism. In 1874 Virchow introduced the first standard procedure for conducting an autopsy that is still used today.

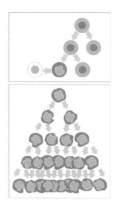

Healthy cell

Diseased cell

Eliminated cell

Left: Virchow's work on the cellular basis of disease showed that while damaged cells are normally eliminated by the body in a process called apoptosis (top left), cancerous cells can evade this system and multiply freely (bottom left).

Virchow was greatly influenced by the work of Matthias Schleiden (1804–1881) and Theodor Schwann (1810–1882), German biologists working on the importance of the cell in biology and medicine. Schleiden claimed that plants were made up of cells, while Schwann had discovered that cells were the basic building blocks of all the animal tissues he studied. Their research led Virchow to believe that disease began in the cells.

He argued that disease and its symptoms either resulted from an abnormality within the cells, or from the cells' response to some kind of stimulus. His work revealed the cellular basis of cancer, which is still the basis of modern views of the disease, where one abnormal cell multiplies to form a tumour.

Virchow was a man of many interests. He was involved in anthropology and archaeology, working on excavations hoping to uncover the ancient Greek city of Troy. He also believed that a doctor could be a vehicle for social reform. He was influential in improving public health in Germany: as a member of Berlin City Council, he advised on a number of issues, including sewage disposal, school hygiene and the inspection of meat.

Gregor Mendel

Although their lifespans overlapped, Gregor Mendel and Charles Darwin never met. But while Darwin was developing a theory of evolution, Mendel found statistical proof that plants and animals pass physical characteristics from one generation to the next.

Born: 1822, Heinzendorf, Austria
Importance: Demonstrated that each physical characteristic was inherited separately
Died: 1884, Brünn, Austrian Empire [Now Brno, Czech Republic]

From the simple observation of livestock and crops, people knew that the offspring of plants or animals showed mixtures of their parents' physical characteristics. In his first paper, *Experiments in Plant Hybridization*, published in 1866, Mendel wrote that he wanted to discover a 'generally applicable law of the formation and development of hybrids'.

He described how he had carefully bred a type of pea, *Pisum sativum*. The plant was cheap and came in many strains that when bred in isolation produced identical offspring, but gave more complex results when mixed to produce hybrids.

Crossing a plant that produced smooth peas with another that produced wrinkled peas gave offspring that all had smooth peas. When these second-generation offspring were interbred, some of the new plants produced smooth, and some wrinkled peas. Intriguingly the ratio was almost perfectly three plants with smooth peas for every one with wrinkled peas.

He then looked at the way different colours were passed from one generation to the next and found that the same rule applied, and noted that inheritance of the colour of both the plant's flowers and its peas occurred independently of pea shape.

Mendel studied with incredible diligence, cultivating some 28,000 pea plants to generate data for just two scientific papers. But it took genius to make sense of the results. Mendel realized that such phenomena could only occur if three things were

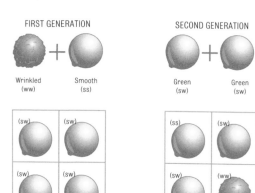

FIRST GENERATION

Wrinkled
(ww)

Smooth
(ss)

(sw)   (sw)

(sw)   (sw)

SECOND GENERATION

Green
(sw)

Green
(sw)

(ss)   (sw)

(sw)   (ww)

Above: As with eye colour in humans, the texture of a pea plant's seeds is determined by a pair of genes. A plant will produce wrinkled peas (ww) only when *both* genes are of the recessive 'wrinkled' variety. Any other combination involving the dominant 'smooth' gene (s) will result in a plant with smooth peas.

happening in the process of reproduction: first, characteristics must be carried from one generation to another by means of some physical 'element' – we now call this element a 'gene'. Secondly, each characteristic must be recorded in the cells on a pair of these elements. Thirdly, Mendel concluded that some of the characteristics were dominant over others.

When Mendel died he was certain that he had made an important discovery and disappointed that no one seemed to care. Recognition only came in 1900 when three other scientists, Dutchman Hugo de Vries (1848–1935), German Carl Correns (1864–1933) and Austrian Erich Tschermak (1871–1962), read Mendel's work. They had each unknowingly repeated his work and discovered similar rules – but Mendel had got there first.

Louis Pasteur

Each of Pasteur's discoveries represents a link in an uninterrupted chain, beginning with asymmetry in molecules, moving through his realization that some micro-organisms cause fermentation in beer and wine – while others lead to diseases – and ending with an understanding of the science behind vaccination.

Born: 1822, Dole, France
Importance: Identified the roles played by bacteria in food and disease
Died: 1895, Saint-Cloud, France

Like so many geniuses, Pasteur did poorly at school, but excelled once he got to university, and by the age of 26 was working on the chemistry and optical properties of asymmetric molecules. He came to the conclusion that although many molecules exist in two forms that are mirror images of each other, if they have been produced by a biological process only one of the forms will be present. If both forms are present, a physical process most probably generated the molecules. Asymmetry differentiates the organic world from the mineral world. In other words, asymmetric molecules are always the product of life forces.

This discovery had an unexpected use when he was asked to solve a problem in a factory that was fermenting beetroot to produce alcohol, because on some occasions the factory instead generated lactic acid. At the time, fermentation was seen as a chemical process that occurred when you brought the right ingredients together: sugar broke down into alcohol as a result of some inherent destabilising vibrations. The yeast cells found in wine were thought to play no role in the process.

Pasteur realized that the lactic acid crystals he observed were all of one type and correctly concluded that they had been created by living organisms. He then realized that while healthy, round yeast cells generated alcohol, lactic acid was being produced by small, rod-like micro-organisms that we now know were bacteria. The solution to the factory owner's problem was to keep everything clean, but the repercussions were that Pasteur realized that microscopic 'germs' could have a significant impact on life.

Later, Pasteur was called in to solve problems in the French silk-worm industry. The worms were either dying, or failing to spin silk. He found that healthy worms became infected when they nested on leaves used by infected worms. Without fully understanding what was going on he solved the problem by recommending certain conditions of temperature, humidity, ventilation and quality of food, as well as husbandry techniques that kept newly-bred worms away from older ones.

Together this would probably have placed Pasteur in the history books, but it was when he realized that diseases such as cholera, diphtheria, scarlet fever, syphilis and smallpox were caused by microbiological agents – germs – that his place in history was assured. Remarkably however, he went further still and showed that injecting heat-damaged bacteria into people made them immune to the disease caused by healthy bacteria. By doing this he invented modern vaccination and triggered a massive advance in the fight against disease.

Yeast: Single-celled organisms that occur naturally, and are used in baking and brewing.

Scarlet fever: A disease that results from infection with a strain of Streptococcus bacteria, spread by respiratory droplets. It carries an erythrogenic (rash-inducing) toxin that causes the skin to shed itself.

Robert Koch

Born the son of a miner, Robert Koch always loved biology, and while studying anthrax he became the first person to demonstrate that specific bacteria caused specific diseases.

Born: 1843, Clausthal, Germany
Importance: Proved the link between bacteria and disease
Died: 1910, Baden-Baden, Germany

While studying medicine Koch was influenced by Professor of Anatomy Jacob Henle (1809–1885), who believed that living, parasitic organisms caused infectious diseases. After briefly serving as a medical officer with the army in the Franco-Prussian war, Koch became the District Medical Officer for the province of Wollstein.

Although he was hard-pressed with his medical duties and cut off from other scientific activity, Koch set up a small laboratory in the four-roomed flat he shared with his wife and young daughter. He started studying anthrax, a disease that was rife among the farm animals in the area. Koch had a hunch that it was associated with a type of bacterium that had recently been discovered.

To start with, he took slivers of wood and spiked them into the spleens of animals that had died of anthrax, and then spiked the wood into mice. The mice became infected with bacteria and died. Mice spiked with wood covered with a healthy animal's blood were unaffected. Clearly something in the infected blood was transmitting the disease.

But was it the bacteria or something else that killed the mice? To answer this, Koch developed ways of culturing bacteria and ensured that he could select some that were several generations away from any that had come from an infected animal. These still caused anthrax. The results showed for the first time that it was these bacteria, and nothing else, that caused the disease.

Recognition among the scientific community eventually led to Koch being given proper laboratory space in Berlin. Here he showed that you could grow bacteria on solid surfaces such as potato and on agar kept in a special flat, round dish designed by his colleague Richard Petri (1852–1921) – a container now known throughout the world as the Petri dish.

As Koch studied, he came up with a list of four features that a micro-organism must satisfy before it can be definitely linked to a disease. 'Koch's postulates' state that you must be able to:

1. *Isolate the organism from every animal that has symptoms of the disease.*
2. *Propagate the bacteria in a laboratory.*
3. *Reproduce the disease by injecting the organism into a suitable recipient.*
4. *Re-isolate the organism from this recipient.*

As his work developed, he travelled widely, investigating diseases in various parts of Europe and Africa. When he died, infectious disease had lost some of its mystery and was now the target of scientific research.

Anthrax: Bacterial infection that can cause a severe disease if it enters via the skin, but is often fatal if the bacteria or its spores are inhaled.

Agar: Gelatinous material, derived from certain marine algae, that is used as a base on which to grow bacteria.

Oswald Avery

Oswald Avery was among the first molecular biologists to suggest that DNA played a significant role in the 'transforming principle', which allowed dead bacteria to pass its virulent properties on to live bacteria. His research stimulated much interest in DNA and eventually led to the discovery that DNA carries the 'life blueprint' for all living organisms.

Born: 1877, Halifax, Canada
Importance: One of the first molecular biologists to discover the properties of DNA
Died: 1955, Nashville, United States

Born in Canada, Avery emigrated to New York at a young age and studied at Colgate University and then Columbia University, where he qualified in medicine in 1904. Although he practised medicine for a while, his real interest was research in microbiology. He took up a post at the Rockefeller Institute in 1913, where he remained for the rest of his long career.

Avery's research focused on the microbes responsible for tuberculosis and pneumonia. He was intrigued by findings reported in 1928 by Fred Griffith, a microbiologist in London. Griffith was working with pneumococci, one of the organisms that could cause pneumonia. There were two types of pneumococci, which Griffith called 'rough' and 'smooth' after the appearance of their colonies when grown on agar medium. The rough bacteria were innocuous, while the smooth ones were virulent. Their smooth appearance came from the presence of a carbohydrate 'coat' around each microbe, which allowed them to evade the immune system and therefore cause disease.

When Griffith mixed live rough pneumococci with dead smooth pneumococci and injected the combination into lab mice, he found it was lethal. He said something, which he called the 'transforming principle', had passed from the dead bacteria, conferring its virulent properties upon the live bacteria. Avery set out to identify this transforming principle.

By the 1940s, it was known that chromosomes – tiny thread-like structures visible in the nucleus under a microscope – carried genetic information, a 'blueprint' of the biochemical and physical characteristics of an organism, although it was not discovered how this worked until the 1960s. Chromosomes were composed of roughly half protein and half deoxyribonucleic acid (DNA).

At the time, protein was considered the more significant part by biochemists, as it is more complex than DNA. Avery spent years trying to pull the transforming principle out of his experimental mixtures in order to determine its chemical identity. He used enzymes to chop up various cell components: if an enzyme removed a cell component and the transforming property was retained in the experiment, then that component could be eliminated. In 1944 he and his colleagues, Colin McLeod and Maclyn Macarty, announced that DNA was the famous transforming principle. Scientists later found that DNA is the basis of all genes, carrying the life blueprint in all organisms from bacteria to humans. In 1953 Francis Crick and James Watson discovered the double-helix structure of DNA, which laid the foundations for an entirely new approach to medicine and biology.

Alexander Fleming

When Alexander Fleming was born, disease-causing bacteria had terrifying power, not because it was stronger or more lethal, but simply because treatments were unreliable at best. At that time, a simple scratch from a rosebush could be enough to kill you.

Born: 1881, Lochfield, Scotland
Importance: Discovered penicillin, the first known antibiotic
Died: 1955, London, England

After spending four years working in a shipping office, Fleming entered St Mary's Medical School and trained to be a doctor. He was soon working with vaccine pioneer Almroth Wright (1861–1947) and started looking for substances that could kill bacteria without harming animal tissues.

Hopes of finding chemical cures for diseases had been raised when in 1909 German chemist-physician Paul Ehrlich (1854–1915) had found a chemical that could treat syphilis. He had tried hundreds of compounds, and 'salvarsan', the 606th, worked. Fleming soon became one of the very few physicians to administer salvarsan in London, and developed such a busy practice, he got the nickname 'Private 606'.

The First World War interrupted his work, but after it ended he made the discovery that tears contain lysozyme, a biological molecule that breaks chemical bonds within the cell walls of some bacteria, causing them to burst. It was a significant discovery, but didn't work on all bacteria.

Fleming kept looking and in 1928, while working on the influenza virus, he made a chance observation. Glancing over a set of discarded Petri dishes, he noted that an area around a growth of mould was cleared of bacteria. He wondered if it could be the mould that was producing a chemical that killed the bacteria and so took a sample to test. He discovered that this mould was a member of the *Penicillium* family, and that it did indeed release chemicals that, even if they were highly diluted, killed bacteria.

The chemical released turns out to inhibit one particular step in the biochemical process used by many bacteria to build their cell walls. Without this process, the bacteria burst as they try to grow. Penicillin is called a bacteriocidal agent because it actively kills growing bacteria, though it must be noted that it doesn't work on all bacteria, as others use a different biochemical process for building their cell walls.

> A good gulp of hot whiskey at bedtime – it's not very scientific, but it helps.
>
> Alexander Fleming

Having discovered this chemical, Fleming did little more with it, but New Zealander Howard Walter Florey (1898–1968) and an interdisciplinary team that included chemist Ernst Boris Chain (1906–1976) succeeded in extracting penicillin and showed that it had great promise as a treatment.

By now the Second World War had broken out and with the Battle of Britain in full swing, Florey set up a processing plant first near Oxford, and then in America. Here Florey came across some mould growing on a lump of rockmelon. This mould produced 3,000 times more penicillin than Fleming's original strain, and American factories were soon making billions of units of penicillin a month.

The discoverer of germ theory, Louis Pasteur, famously said that 'fortune favours the prepared mind', a saying which certainly held true for both Fleming and Florey.

Barbara McClintock

Before scientists knew the structure of DNA, and while they still had no idea how it carried information, Barbara McClintock's theory that genes could break free and move around within the chromosomes set genetics on a new path of discovery.

Born: 1902, Hartford, USA
Importance: Discovered that some genes are able to move around the chromosomes
Died: 1992, Huntington, New York

As McClintock started her research, scientists thought that the dumb-bell-shaped features inside each cell's nucleus probably carried biological information, and that these 'chromosomes' somehow managed to pass the information to new individual cells during the process of cell division. Scientists also believed that traits such as the colour of a flower and the shape of a pea could be inherited separately, because during the cell division that generates pollen and seeds (or sperm and eggs in animals), parts of the various chromosomes physically broke off and swapped with each other. It was a suggestion, but there was no evidence to support it.

Shortly after receiving her doctorate in 1927, McClintock began work with Harriet Creighton (1909–2004) at Cornell University, New York. McClintock started by working out ways of identifying the ten different chromosomes present in maize cells. Then, working with a particular strain of maize, *Zea Mays*, that had a mutated chromosome number nine, the two researchers showed that parts of the chromosome did indeed swap over during the process that generates reproductive cells.

Next, working with Lewis Stadler (1869–1954) at the University of Missouri, McClintock started studying maize that had been exposed to X-rays. Peering into their cells with her microscope, she identified ring chromosomes. These she correctly suggested were parts of chromosomes that had been broken by radiation and subsequently fused to form a ring. Chromosomes occur in cells in pairs, and McClintock saw that chromosomes could break and fuse with the other member of the pair, before being ripped apart when the cell divided – a phenomenon that became known as the breakage-fusion-bridge cycle.

Moving to Cold Spring Harbor, McClintock discovered a bizarre genetic behaviour in some of her breakage-fusion-bridge strains. Certain genes appeared to move from cell to cell during development of the corn kernel. When she presented this data at a meeting in 1951 she expected recognition and acceptance, but instead was greeted with silence and some derision. As she said in her Nobel prize acceptance speech, 'Because I became actively involved in the subject of genetics only 21 years after the rediscovery, in 1900, of Mendel's principles of heredity. . . acceptance of these principles was not general among biologists'.

The problem was that many of the powerful people in science backed a theory of genetics that suggested that the function of a gene depended on where it was in a chromosome. If that were the case, then genes just couldn't jump around; or if they did, they would cease to function. McClintock's data only made sense if genes were distinct units that could move around on their own but still function. In time McClintock was proved right, and her theory of the nature of genes underpins current genetics.

Gene: The segment of DNA on a chromosome that contains the information necessary to make a particular protein.

Chromosome: A threadlike package of genes in the nucleus of a cell, made of DNA wrapped around supporting proteins.

Crick and Watson

The names Crick and Watson are so firmly linked together that it almost seems they are one person. Their joint fame rests on their momentous announcement, in 1953, of their discovery of the structure of DNA.

Francis Crick
Born: 1916, Northampton, England
Importance: Discovered the structure of DNA
Died: 2004, San Diego, USA

James Watson
Born: 1928, Chicago, USA
Importance: Discovered the structure of DNA

When they first met in Cambridge, England, in 1951, Francis Crick and James Watson shared a common curiosity: how to fathom the structure of a curious biological molecule called deoxyribonucleic acid (DNA). Crick had joined the Medical Research Council research group in Cambridge two years earlier, where he began to study the structure of proteins by crystallizing them, passing a beam of X-rays through the crystal, and then analysing the resulting diffraction pattern that was projected onto a sheet of photographic paper.

By now, scientists were sure that the information about the structure of an organism was stored in a cell's nucleus, passed on from cell to cell as an organism grows, and from parent to offspring in eggs and sperm. There was increasing evidence that the material inside the cell enabling this to occur was DNA, but a fundamental mystery remained: how could any biological molecule store enough information to guide the development of cells, organs and indeed entire organisms, in a cell that is smaller than a full stop?

As a sideline to their main projects, Crick and Watson started to consider the structure of DNA. Their interest was enhanced after Watson attended a seminar in London where researcher Rosalind Franklin (1920–1958) presented some cross-shaped X-ray diffraction pictures of DNA that indicated that the molecule had a helical structure.

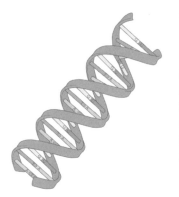

Left: The DNA molecule looks like a spiral ladder where the rungs are formed by base molecules, which occur in pairs. These sequences of base pairs represent the genetic information stored in the DNA.

From chemical analysis of DNA, Watson and Crick knew that it consisted of four different components called 'bases', and made scale models of each base. They also realized that these bases could form chains, and so they tried building a triple helical arrangement of the components with the spiralling spine formed in the middle, and the rest of the bases pointing out.

The model didn't work, but in 1953 Watson got a sneak-preview of another of Franklin's X-ray diffraction images and realized that the pattern could best be explained by DNA being a *double* helix, with the two strands running in opposing directions.

Crick and Watson jumped to a radical conclusion: the two chains were effectively mirror images of each other. Each chain held equivalent information, and you could produce a second copy by separating the chains and using each as a template. Genetics came of age.

The following 50 years saw a steady increase in the number of techniques that are enabling scientists to make sense of the genetic processes going on inside every living cell. The 21st century will see them harness that activity.

Rosalind Franklin

Combining her knowledge of chemistry and physics, Rosalind Franklin was an expert X-ray crystallographer, which allowed her to delve into the structures of previously mysterious chemicals and viruses. Most notably, her skills provided clear images of deoxyribonucleic acid (DNA) and its double helix structure.

Born: 25 July 1920, London, England
Importance: Advanced scientific understanding of the structures of DNA, RNA, viruses, coal and graphite
Died: 16 April 1958, London, England

After her undergraduate degree, Franklin began working for the British Coal Utilisation Research Association (BCURA) where she discovered the molecular structure of coal in order to accurately estimate the performance of different coal types. Franklin continued this work in Paris after the Second World War, but went on to use X-ray crystallography to study the structures in more precise detail.

X-ray crystallography shoots X-rays at a crystal which, depending on the specific structure of the crystal, will be deflected in a specific way. Franklin looked at how the X-rays were bent and calculated what the molecular structure must be.

Franklin later switched her focus from coal to her most notable research, the structure of DNA. Building and refining her own X-ray crystallography experiment specifically designed to study DNA, she spent her time creating sharper and clearer images. While several theories for the complicated structure were circulating, there was not enough known about DNA to favour any one in particular. However, Franklin's preliminary results were already enough not only to calculate the density of DNA but also to suggest a helical shape. In 1953, Franklin's famous 'Image 51' provided the conclusive evidence that the structure of DNA was two strands wound around each other in the now well-known double helix structure.

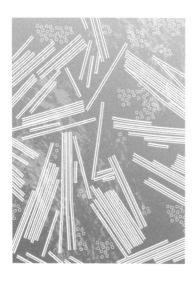

Left: Tobacco mosaic virus was the first pathogen identified as a virus. It is named for the distinctive mosaic-type mottling it causes on leaves.

Franklin went on to use her X-ray crystallography skills to study the structure of ribonucleic acid (RNA) within many plant viruses. Franklin began with the tobacco mosaic virus (TMV), finding it to be long cylindrical tubes of the same length, contrary to understanding of the time. She later went on to prove the RNA structure within TMV had a similar structure to DNA but instead of two strands in the double helix, RNA was a long single strand that could loop back on itself. This result helped her ultimately determine that the structure of TMV was a hollow tube with the RNA wound around. With her research group at Birkbeck, University of London, Franklin went on to study plant viruses affecting potatoes, turnips, tomatoes and peas. Towards the end of her life, she moved onto the polio virus, bravely studying a live form of the virus while it was in a crystal state.

Franklin used her unparalleled experimental skills as an X-ray crystallographer in a range of settings to help science discover the structure of life and the famous double helix responsible for coding our genetics.

Jennifer Doudna

By repurposing pieces of a bacterium, Jennifer Doudna created a gene editing technique so easy grade-schoolers can use it. Her breakthrough poured accelerant on biological research – and the ethical debates that surround it.

Born: 19 February 1964, Washington, DC
Importance: Invented the CRISPR/Cas9 gene-editing technique

In 2012, at age 49, Jennifer Doudna helped discover a simple way to change the genetic code inside living cells. The method, which carries the unwieldy moniker CRISPR/Cas9, can make precise modifications in the DNA of microbes, mushrooms, mammals and more. In the years since the discovery, Doudna's tool has been adopted by thousands of scientists around the world, including some interested in modifying the human race.

Doudna earned her doctorate at Harvard University in the laboratory of Jack Szostak (1952–), who would later receive a Nobel Prize for his research on molecular biology.

> The power to control our species' genetic future is awesome and terrifying. Deciding how to handle it may be the biggest challenge we have ever faced.
>
> Jennifer Doudna

Together they provided early evidence that RNA, a molecular cousin of DNA, may have played a central role in the emergence of life on Earth. RNA is a unique biomolecule in that it can both store genetic information and catalyze chemical reactions; as a graduate student, Doudna studied how naturally occurring RNA molecules perform chemical catalysis.

Before starting her own RNA research laboratory at Yale, Doudna worked as a postdoctoral researcher with Tom Cech (1947–), a Nobel laureate who had recently helped discover the existence of RNA-based catalysts. Doudna used powerful electron microscopes to study the structures of these enigmatic molecules with Cech, then later as an independent researcher at Yale.

In 2002 Doudna relocated her laboratory to the University of California at Berkeley. There she turned her formidable attention towards an obscure puzzle involving bacteria. She and other researchers eventually showed that pieces of bacterial RNA and other bacterial enzymes could be combined together to produce scissor-like molecules that physically cut DNA. By modifying the RNA component, they showed that the molecular scissors could be targeted to specific regions within a gene to produce precise modifications. In nature, bacteria use this system to defeat viruses.

RNA: A single-stranded molecule that plays an essential role in coding, regulating and expressing genes. Along with DNA it is a macromolecule necessary for all known forms of life.

Previous gene editing techniques were expensive, inaccurate and complex to use. Doudna's new method was cheap, accurate and relatively simple. Because of this, the method quickly spread into laboratories and classrooms around the world. It also earned Doudna numerous awards and international celebrity status.

Because CRISPR/Cas9 gene editing can modify the DNA inside human cells, some scientists – including Doudna herself – believe it may have a role to play in mitigating genetic disease. Scientists are investigating whether it can be used to erase cancer, muscular dystrophy, sickle cell disease and more. But this would involve making genetic changes to human beings, either before or after they are born, thus opening the door to concerns over eugenics, healthcare inequality and other unforeseen consequences.

Index

References to scientists are given only where mentioned other than their main entry.

128